Total Training
For Rugby Fitness

Graham Lowe

and

Glenn Jenkins

Photography by
David Jenkins

Published by

Speed Power and Stability Systems Ltd

Christchurch, New Zealand

© 2005

Speed Power and Stability Systems Ltd

Design and typeset by Go Ahead Graphics, Christchurch.

Printed by Saxon Print, Christchurch.

ISBN

0476009227

Special Thank you to

Hiroshi Nagano

Foreward

"The fitness drills in this book have definitely worked for me.
If you want to get bigger, faster, stronger and fitter for rugby….buy it. The programmes have given me the speed and power I needed to get to the top and stay ahead of the competition during my professional career. The exercises and programmes are a revolution in rugby fitness and I am glad to see that young players and coaches can now learn these drills. I wish I had known these secrets earlier in my career and thank Graham and Glenn for getting me on track with my fitness and speed."

Tana Umaga
International Rugby Player

About the Authors

Graham Lowe

Graham is recognised as New Zealand's leading and most successful professional rugby trainer. His career began in Dunedin where he completed a Masters Degree in Physical Education and was personal trainer to a number of elite rugby players.

His trainers position with the Wellington Lions from 1997-2001 (NPC Champions 2000), Hurricanes from 1999-2001, Auckland Blues (the 2003 Super 12 Champions) and currently working at the very highest international level, has seen him responsible for developing the fitness of world class players including Tana Umaga, Christian Cullen and Taine Randell.

Graham's reputation now sees his cutting edge training techniques being embraced by countless trainers, coaches, and players all around the world. There is no-one better qualified to offer players of all levels quality fitness training guidance. This book is the culmination of years of theoretical study and 10 years as a professional trainer at the very highest level with many of the best players in the world.

Glenn Jenkins

Glenn is a specialist in the development of performance speed for sport. His 15 years experience in the field has included the design and development of new and cutting edge speed training aids.

He has worked at an international level with six different sports and was Tana Umaga's speed coach from 1996-2000. Glenn has presented international training seminars in the field of speed development in many countries including New Zealand, Australia, Japan, South Africa and Europe.

He is the founding director of Speed Power & Stability Systems Ltd - an award winning export company specialising in sports performance, with the speed enhancement systems developed within the organization now stretching into 12 countries.

Glenn is the writer and producer of six sports training videos including the best selling Quickness & Agility for Sport series and has published articles in fitness and sporting magazines.

Introduction

Congratulations on purchasing this book. You have taken the first step towards improved rugby performance. The aim of the information contained in this book is to stimulate your mind and present some of the many different ways you can train to physically prepare yourself to become a better rugby player. It will help you achieve your performance goals and combines photographic descriptions with a variety of training options that will enhance your current knowledge and training experience.

The guide will start with a section detailing how to get started, including a fitness testing explanation to ensure that you use activities contained in the later sections to best suit your personal training goal.

A chapter has been dedicated to each specific component of rugby fitness with many training options clearly explained for easy understanding. The final chapter explains the planning and periodisation advice that will allow you to complete the training options in a way that will maximise your fitness gains.

This training guide is designed as an easy to use, informative package which will optimize your rugby fitness preparation. It does not intend to provide all the answers. Your training experience and open mind will determine what you gain from the information presented.

Before You Start

Before you start training in preparation for the coming season, it is important that you create some short and long term, achievable goals for your season. In other words, what do you want to achieve from your rugby season? These goals might be as follows:

- To have a strong running base that enables you to achieve a high tackle count or hit high numbers of rucks

- To have an improved strength base that enhances your scrummaging ability and improves your hitting and cleanouts around the ruck

- To improve your lateral speed and ability to beat your man

- To improve your anaerobic (repeated-speed) fitness so your support play as a loose forward or as a winger, means you are more likely to turn up in the right place at the right time.

An important part of your goal setting for rugby fitness is to have some measures of fitness. Obviously the chosen testing programme needs to relate to the components of fitness that relate to rugby, as they will be explained in the later chapters in this guide.

The next section of this chapter will provide some fitness testing options and explain why they are good options to test your current fitness.

Good Luck!

Contents

Fitness Testing

Feedback is the Food of Champions

A key factor in your choice of testing procedures is to ensure that you re-test to ensure that results accurately indicate any improvement in your fitness. This is called a reliable and repeatable test. There are a huge number of tests that can be performed. The procedures that are included in this section are termed field tests because they can be done outside, there is no particular cost associated with performing them, and they have good reliability. Undertaking the following fitness testing battery will help show whether all your hard work has had any affect on your fitness measures.

Components of Rugby Fitness and How to Test Them

Traditional Field Based Fitness Testing For Rugby

Fitness testing is one of the most controversial areas of preparation in relation to rugby.

When considering what type of fitness testing procedures to undertake, the reliability and validity of the tests are crucial. A reliable test is one that can be replicated in identical conditions with all variables remaining consistent for re-testing. For example, on Monday and Friday a player completes the test and achieves the same result.

A consistent testing environment will ensure that when a player scores a different result you can have faith that the higher or lower measure is an indication of changes to fitness or attitude. An unreliable measure may be gained if changes to environment are present at the time of retesting. For example, floor surface, running surface, grass length and condition, wind, temperature etc.

A valid test is one that measures what you want it to measure. The challenge with rugby is that if you want the test to be more representative of the fitness required in a rugby game then the reliability tends to suffer. In a game you sprint, tackle, jog, run, scrum, ruck and maul etc. and as such testing for all these factors becomes very complicated.

Rugby requires high levels of running, speed, agility, power and strength (to name a few factors) and it is possible to measure / test changes in these factors in relative isolation. Something else to consider with fitness testing is that you may wish to test what you train. By recording your weights as you lift them, and key running sessions as you do them you will have at your fingertips an ongoing measure of your fitness.

The fitness testing components to follow have been selected because they are easy to perform, have considerable normative data available, and give basic accurate information upon which to base your training around.

Component of fitness	Test	How to perform	Why is this test good?	Other options
Aerobic Base	3000m time trial	This test requires a 400m running track and a stop watch. The test is as simple as the time taken to cover 3000m. For the test to be reliable you should consider wind and the condition of the track if it is grass. Look at Table 3 for comparative data and targets for different positions.	It costs nothing to perform, is reliable, and gives an indication of your ability to run which is important in rugby.	You may chose a shorter distance such as 2400m and create your own comparative data (i.e. compare times to yourself). The Beep Test is an option but requires a beep tape, and tape recorder.
Combined Energy Systems	100m-400m-1600m	This test requires a 400m running track and a stop watch. After a comprehensive warm up the player performs a **timed 100m**, rests for 12-15 minutes, a **timed 400m**, rests for 12-15 minutes and then completes a **timed 1600m.** For the test to be reliable you should consider wind and the condition of the track if it is grass.	It costs nothing to perform, is reliable, and gives more information about your different energy systems and how you might respond to different types of training.	None available
Leg Strength	2-5RM Squat	RM stands for Repetition Maximum and means the maximum weight you can lift that many times. In other words it is the maximum weight you can lift in a squat movement 2 to 5 times. *Caution: You must perform the movement correctly and have a partner to spot you.*	The squat is considered to be a key strength exercise for whole body strength.	The squat can be performed with a higher RM target if you have limited training experience. For example 10 repetitions. It is important to master the technique before increasing the load.

Component of fitness	Test	How to perform	Why is this test good?	Other options
Leg Power	Standing Vertical Jump	The vertical jump test measures the difference between your standing vertical reach and your maximum vertical jump. All you need is a wall, some chalk, and a measuring tape. Reach as high up the wall as you can and mark with chalk. Then jump beside the wall with feet shoulder width apart and measure the difference between the two marks. This is your vertical jump.	An easily repeated and cheap method for testing leg power.	The Power Clean could be used as an indication of whole body power. However good training experience and good technique is essential.
Upper Body Strength	2-5RM Bench Press	This test is again the maximum weight you can lift in a bench press movement 2 to 5 times. *Caution: You must perform the movement correctly and have a partner to spot you.*	Still a key upper body exercise. Easily repeatable and reliable.	A medicine ball toss maybe used to give an indication of upper body explosive power.
Upper Body Strength	Pull Ups (Weighted) 2-5RM	This test requires a chinning bar and is the maximum amount of complete chin ups you can complete using a load that only allows you to finish 2 to 5 reps. The arms must be straight at the bottom and the chin must reach the bar at the top of the movement. A shoulder width grip with the palms facing you allows for better reliability. Weighted Vests are ideal to add extra load.	An indication of arm and back strength. Also creates awareness of body weight and will challenge your grip strength.	A Bentover Row would be far more valid to rugby but it has poor reliability due to differences in technique. This exercise is an example of why finding valid measures of pulling strength is quite challenging.
Speed	10m/20m 30m/40m	Requires a set of timing lights to get truly accurate times. Hand timing a 40m sprint can result in up to +/- 0.3sec inaccuracy in the recorded result. It is important to standardise the start position, distance from the first speed gate, and the height of the gates. A tape measure will ensure that your distances are correct every time. It is worthwhile looking at your 20m (forwards/halfbacks) and 30m times (backs). You are far more inclined to run these distances during a rugby game than 40m.	If you have access to timing lights it is a great way of measuring your straight line speed performance.	Agility is a critical component of rugby performance but can be quite unreliable to measure and has the added challenge of ensuring that the direction changes are valid to rugby. A difficult component to test.

Fitness Standards for Rugby Fitness Tests

2-5RM Squat kg

Position	Beginnner	Intermediate	Advanced
Tight Forwards	130 (2-5) reps	150 (2-5)	170 (2-5)
Loose Forwards	120 (2-5)	140 (2-5)	160 (2-5)
Inside Backs	100 (2-5)	120 (2-5)	140 (2-5)
Outside Backs	110 (2-5)	130 (2-5)	150 (2-5)

Vertical Jump

	Beginnner	Intermediate	Advanced
Tight Forwards	0.4 - 0.45m	0.45 - 0.5m	0.5 - 0.55m
Loose Forwards	0.45 - 0.5m	0.5 - 0.55m	0.55 - 0.6m
Inside Backs	0.5 - 0.55m	0.55 - 0.6m	0.6 - 0.65m
Outside Backs	0.55 - 0.6m	0.6 - 0.65m	0.6 - 0.70m

2-5RM Bench Press

Position	Beginnner	Intermediate	Advanced
Tight Forwards	100 (2-5) reps	120 (2-5)	140 (2-5)
Loose Forwards	90 (2-5)	110 (2-5)	130 (2-5)
Inside Backs	70 (2-5)	90 (2-5)	110 (2-5)
Outside Backs	80 (2-5)	100 (2-5)	120 (2-5)

Pull Ups (Weighted) 2-5RM

	Beginnner	Intermediate	Advanced
Tight Forwards	0kg	10kg	20kg
Loose Forwards	5kg	20kg	30kg
Inside Backs	10kg	20kg	30kg
Outside Backs	10kg	20kg	30kg

3000m Time Trial

Position	Begin.	Inter.	Adv.
Tight Forwards	<13.30	<13.00	<12.30
Loose Forwards	<13.00	<12.30	<12.00
Inside Backs	<12.20	<12.00	<11.40
Outside Backs	<12.30	<12.10	<11.50

10m Speed

	Begin.	Inter.	Adv.
Tight Forwards	<1.90	<1.85	<1.80
Loose Forwards	<1.85	<1.80	<1.75
Inside Backs	<1.80	<1.75	<1.70
Outside Backs	<1.80	<1.75	<1.70

40m Speed

	Begin.	Inter.	Adv.
Tight Forwards	<5.70	<5.60	<5.50
Loose Forwards	<5.50	<5.40	<5.30
Inside Backs	<5.30	<5.20	<5.10
Outside Backs	<5.25	<5.15	<5.05

NOTE: One of the key factors in fitness targets is that it is more important to improve than to reach a target. Targets are based on large numbers of people and do not count for individual variations. As such they should be thought of as guidelines with each individual focussing on being the best that they can be and making positive progress.

The Future of Fitness Testing for Rugby

With traditional fitness testing the focus has been on monitoring the individual facets of fitness required for rugby. Consequently tests such as the Beep Test and the 3000m time trial have dominated the landscape for a long time.

In more recent times there has been a drive towards testing that encompasses multiple energy systems and includes other components of rugby. An example would be getting down and up off the ground. Agility and high speed is being looked at rather than just straight line speed, and strength and power are considered either in a traditional sense via the weight room or in a field based setting using medicine balls, powerbags and plyometric type activities.

Testing varies from country to country and from sport to sport. Generally speaking recent trends have been made to move away from athletics dominated fitness tests in team sports to more sport specific tests. As such there tends to be less normative data on this type of testing as there is less history, but what is important to consider is that the change in the individual athlete and their performance should always be the dominant factor moving ahead.

As our understanding of the demands of rugby increase and the demands of rugby change due to the increasing size and speed of the player so the requirements of fitness testing needs to move with it. Technology has changed dramatically with the advent of GPS (Global Positioning Systems) allowing sports people at all levels to gain a deeper understanding of the demands of their sport and training. Heart rate monitors are becoming more sophisticated, significantly cheaper and more available than in the past.

Key Summary Points

1. You are an individual and as such you should be looking to be the best you can be before you worry about what other people are doing and achieving.

2. It is important that you attempt to understand the game that you are playing. To train smart and play well you need to have this in mind. Rugby is a stop-start game of high intensity that involves repeated bouts of high intensity activity such as sprinting, scrummaging, tackling, getting down and up off the ground, agility and periods of static work. You need to apply this thinking to your training and fitness testing.

3. The primary goal of fitness testing is to help you train more effectively and provide feedback on fitness changes and areas that require work. It can be very motivational if you approach it with the right attitude.

Individual fitness testing sheet to record results and set goals

Example Recording Sheet

NAME _Joe Bloggs_   DATE _1/11/05_   POSITION _Hooker_

FITNESS TEST	Date	Result	Target	Target Achieved	Date	Result	Target	Goal Achieved
10m Speed	Nov-05	1.79	<1.80	Y	Feb-06	1.77	<1.80	Y
40m Speed	Nov-05	5.39	<5.40	Y	Feb-06	5.41	<5.40	N
_100m_,400m,1600m Time Trial	Nov-05	12.4	<12.5	Y	Feb-06			
100m,_400m_,1600m Time Trial	Nov-05	55s	<53s	Y	Feb-06			
100m,400m,_1600m_ Time Trial	Nov-05	5m 50s	<5m35s	N	Feb-06			
Leg Power (Vertical Jump)	Nov-05	62cm	>60cm	Y				
Back Squat (2-5RM)	Nov-05	170 x 2	> 160 x 2	Y				
Bench Press (2-5RM)	Nov-05	105 x 3	> 120 x 3	N				
Chins (Weighted) 2-5RM	Nov-05	15 x 3	> 30 x 3	N				

Example Evaluation & Analysis Sheet

FITNESS TEST	Date Achieved	Result	Target	Target	Action Required Adjustments	Time Frame	Programming
10m Speed	Nov-05	1.79	<1.80	Y		6 weeks	1 x Speed Agility Maintenance
40m Speed	Nov-05	5.39	<5.40	Y		6 weeks	1 x Speed Agility Maintenance
_100m_, 400m,1600m Time Trial	Nov-05	12.4	<12.5	Y			
100m,_400m_,1600m Time Trial	Nov-05	55s	<60s	Y			
100m,400m, _1600m_ Time Trial	Nov-05	5m 50s	<5m35s	N	High Intensity Base Work	6 weeks	2 sessions week 1 x hill repeats 1 x medium intervals
Leg Power (Vertical Jump)	Nov-05	62cm	>60cm	Y			
Back Squat (2-5RM)	Nov-05	170 x 2	> 160 x 2	Y	Maintenance	6 weeks	
Bench Press (2-5RM)	Nov-05	105 x 3	> 120 x 3	N	Upper Body Strength	6 weeks	2-3 sessions week
Chins (Weighted) 2-5RM	Nov-05	15 x 3	> 30 x 3	N	Upper Body Strength		

Blank Evaluation & Analysis Sheet - Please photocopy for use

Example Recording Sheet

NAME _____   DATE _____   POSITION _____

FITNESS TEST	Date	Result	Target	Target Achieved	Date	Result	Target	Goal Achieved
10m Speed								
40m Speed								
100m,400m,1600m Time Trial								
100m,*400m*,1600m Time Trial								
100m,400m,*1600m* Time Trial								
Leg Power (Vertical Jump)								
Back Squat (2-5RM)								
Bench Press (2-5RM)								
Chins (Weighted) 2-5RM								

Blank Evaluation & Analysis Sheet - Please photocopy for use

FITNESS TEST	Date Achieved	Result	Target	Target	Action Required Adjustments	Time Frame	Programming
10m Speed							
40m Speed							
_100m_, 400m,1600m Time Trial							
100m, _400m_,1600m Time Trial							
100m,400m, _1600m_ Time Trial							
Leg Power (Vertical Jump)							
Back Squat (2-5RM)							
Bench Press (2-5RM)							
Chins (Weighted) 2-5RM							

Running for Rugby Fitness - Aerobic Conditioning

Running is an integral part of rugby. Obviously running does not all occur on the field at the same speed. As a result the running options you decide to use should account for this.

Running Training Tips

- Gradually build up your running volumes. Run every second day to start.
- Don't always repeat the same run. To keep getting improvements your body and mind require variety. Challenge yourself with different routes, intensities, distances and time run.
- A heart rate monitor or GPS system provides good biofeedback and is a worthwhile investment.
- Repeating the same run once every 2-4 weeks provides a good indication of whether your training is improving.
- Running (training) with others can be very motivational. Pick a partner who pushes your buttons e.g. motivates you with good conversation, is self motivated, and has similar ability.

Expert Comment

Functional analysis of the demands of rugby:

Rugby requires high degrees of physical strength in the form of mobile wrestling, relatively high aerobic and anaerobic (repeated-speed) fitness, and combinations of pushing, pulling, lifting, speed and lateral agility.

The ability to handle high velocity impact with other bodies must also be considered. Combining these requirements with the skills of passing and kicking makes for an exciting challenge in the creation of a functional and specific session.

Running Training Options

1. Aerobic Conditioning (Continuous and Fartlek):

The base aerobic conditioning you build will allow your body to adapt better to all the training that follows. The idea is to progress from a higher volume of running at lower speeds into higher intensity running at greater speed as the season approaches.

These aerobic and aerobic interval options have wide time and heart rate ranges due to individual variations in maximum heart rate, training history and ability. The runs get progressively harder by increasing the running speed and by the addition of hill running.

A1 – Long, slow continuous running

- 35-50 minute run at a steady pace
- Course chosen can be relatively flat or include some undulating terrain e.g. a botanical gardens
- Target heart rate will be 150-170 beats/min
- This option should only be used in your transition. Think of this as a method to kick start your running rather than a preferred training method for rugby

A2 – Shorter, faster, continuous running

- 25-35 minute run at a quicker pace
- That is at a quicker pace than the longer run
- The target heart rate should be 155-180 beats/min
- A different running route than the longer one will be required

A3 – Fartlek type hill running

- Run a 5 minute warm-up and then stretch
- Follow with a 25-40 minute run on a hilly road or track
- Work hard on the uphill parts and target a heart rate of 170+ beats/min
- Use the flat areas to recover by running slower
- This run can be as hard or as easy as you make it

A4 – Shorter, faster split run (out and back)

- Run a 5 minute warm-up and then stretch
- Follow with a 10-20 minute run, stop and stretch for 3-5 minutes then run back for 10-20 minutes
- Target heart rate is 150-170 beats/min or at the fastest pace you can maintain for each 10-20 minute block
- If you are running out and back, you should try to run your return more quickly

A5 – Aerobic intervals (40 minutes)

- Run a 5 minute warm-up, and then stretch. Then run for:
  - 9 minutes hard followed by 3 minutes easy
  - 6 minutes hard followed by 2 minutes easy
  - 3 minutes hard followed by 1 minutes easy
  - 6 minutes hard followed by 2 minutes easy
  - 9 minutes hard followed by 3 minutes easy
- This is a 3 work to 1 rest ratio. This ratio can be 2:1 or 1:1 depending on your level of fitness

A6 – *Aerobic intervals (44 minutes)*
- Run a 5-minute warm-up, then stretch. Then complete the following:
  - 5 minutes medium pace
  - 24 minutes (2 minutes hard – 2 minutes easy)
  - 10 minutes easy pace to finish
- Heart rate should be 175+ in the hard blocks
- You can do a similar pattern using 3 minute or 1 minute hard/easy patterns also

2. Repeated-Speed (Intervals):

Repeated-Speed (Intervals) are commonly used in conditioning for many team sports (e.g. soccer, rugby, hockey, netball). You can adjust the distances and rest intervals to suit the demands of rugby, or the stage of your programme and preparation. To see examples of some repeated speed programmes refer to programmes RS1-RS3 in the back of this section.

Interval sessions are best performed on a grass track but an artificial surface increases your consistency through the effects of weather. Recording your heart rate and time to complete each interval gives you important feedback on your training response. Most interval sessions will contain less than 5000m.

The table on the opposite page contains positional target times.

RS1 – *Long interval training*
- Run a 6-8 minute warm-up and stretch.
- 3-4 x 1500m (rest of 5-6 minutes between each run)

RS2 – *Medium long interval training*
- Run a 6-8 minute warm-up and stretch.
- 4-5 x 1000m (rest of 4-5 minutes between each run)

RS3 – *Medium long interval training*
- Run a 6-8 minute warm-up and stretch.
- 4 x 600m (rest for 3 minutes between each run)
- Rest for 5 minutes.
- 4 x 300m (rest for 3 minutes between each run)

RS4 – *Short-medium interval training*
- 6 x 300m (rest for 2mins 30secs between each run)
- Rest for 4 minutes.
- 6 x 150m (rest for 1 minute between each run)

RS5 – *Short interval training*
- 12-20 x 50m sprint (8-9 seconds)/50m jog (repeat every 45 seconds)
- Starting at the goal line of a rugby field, sprint 50m in 8-9 seconds (nearly

full sprint) then jog through to the other end. You have what is left of 45 seconds to recover. Turn around and run back the other way. The target is 10 repeats. The goal is to maintain near maximal speed (i.e. 8-9sec) for each 50m sprint.
- Rest for 4 minutes.
- 12-20 x 50m sprint (8-9 seconds)/50m jog (repeat every 45 seconds)
- Rest for 4 minutes.
- 5 x 100m sprint (18sec) (repeat every 60 seconds)

RS6 - *Short interval training*
- 12-20 x 50m sprint (8-9 seconds)/50m jog (repeat every 45 seconds)
- Rest for 4 minutes.
- 20 x 25m sprint (5-6 seconds)/25m jog (repeat every 20 seconds)
- Rest for 4 minutes.
- 5 x 100m sprint (18sec) (repeat every 60 seconds)

RS7 - *Very short interval training*
- 20 x 25m sprint (5-6 seconds)/25m jog (repeat every 20 seconds)
- Rest for 4 minutes.
- 20 x 25m sprint (5-6 seconds)/25m jog (repeat every 20 seconds)
- Rest for 4 minutes.
- 5 x 50m sprint (8-9 seconds)/50m jog (repeat every 45 seconds)

3. Functional Endurance (aerobic running/cross-training):

Functional endurance is a term applied to any session that includes the specific fitness requirements of a sport (or challenge). It combines a number of different movement patterns with running to create a fitness response that is unique to that sport. You need to think about the specific challenges of your sport and apply them in a circuit type structure. The FE1 programme in the back of this section gives an example of a functional session for rugby.

FE1 - *Functional rugby session (rugby)*
General warm-up for 6-8 minutes, stretch and then continue
- Run hard for 3 minutes, and then walk for 2 minutes
- Ball wrestle/rip with partner (20 sec. each holding the ball)
- Run hard for 2 minutes immediately followed by 2 minutes jogging
- Perform 4 x 30m hills sprints walking down between each one
- Run hard for 1 minute followed by 1 minute walking
- Do a 5m, 10m, 15m and back shuttles series (alternate with a partner to provide rest) repeat this four times
- Run hard for 1 minute followed by 1 minute walking
- Wrestle on knees with partner for 30 seconds
- Run hard for 2 minutes followed by 2 minutes jogging
- Down and ups on the spot x 20 followed by 10 press-ups
- Run hard for 1 minute followed by a 1minute walk to recover
- Run hard for 3 minutes, jog for 2 minutes, walk for 2 minutes, stretch to finish

Positional Target times

Interval Distance	Tight Forwards	Loose Forwards	Backs
Target 1500m time	6min 15sec - 6min 30sec	6min - 6min 15sec	5min 45sec - 6min
Target 1000m time	4min 05sec - 4min 15sec	3min 45sec - 4min 05sec	3min 30sec - 3min 45sec
Target 800m time	3min 15sec - 3min 30sec	3min - 3min 15 sec	2min 45sec - 3min
Target 600m time	2min 15sec - 2min 25sec	2min 5sec - 2min 15sec	1min 55sec - 2min 5sec
Target 400m time	1min 35sec - 1min 40sec	1min 30sec - 1min 35sec	1min 20sec - 1min 30sec
Target 300m time	1min - 1min 10sec	55 sec - 1min 5sec	50sec - 1min
Target 150m time	27sec - 30sec	25sec - 27sec	23sec - 25sec
Target 100m time	16sec - 18sec	15sec - 17sec	14sec - 16sec

Rugby Speed and Agility

Guest Section written by Glenn Jenkins

Speed and agility are well recognised as key rugby performance areas. The modern game has evolved with very well organised defensive screens becoming more and more difficult to breach either in clear line breaks or simply getting over the advantage line to go forward.

The game has sped up dramatically over recent times both in general passages of play and the athleticism of players. Speed is more than ever a huge asset for any player at any level and is a real performance measure. Rugby players with superior speed and agility to their opposition have a definite advantage in all aspects of attacking and defending.

Explosive speed and agility are huge game breaking performance skills that must be trained.

Often the ability of a team to break the line on attack will come down to the athletic ability of an attacker against the athletic ability of a defender.

Speed and agility will determine the attackers ability to evade or beat the defender to find space.

Conversely the defenders ability to react with speed and agility will determine their ability to close down space and be in a position to make the tackle or take space away from any attacking support players.

Most coaches have adopted the *"train the way we play"* philosophy for skill development and unit training in terms of intensity, structure, team patterns and technique. However the same philosophy is rarely applied when considering speed and agility development.

A common mistake made is to implement only conventional track and field based straight line speed development techniques. Unfortunately track and field as a sport has very little physical similarities to the requirements of rugby and as such the training modalities do not effectively develop the well rounded multidirectional movement requirements of the sport.

Generally speaking rugby players are not track sprinters

Applying only track and field grounded training does not fit with the *"train the way we play"* philosophy for a number of reasons.

Rugby Speed vs. Track Sprinting Speed

Multidirectional vs. Linear Straight Line Speed
Rugby is very dynamic, unpredictable and requires a combination of multidirectional movements to be performed at rapid speeds under pressure. Players must move quickly in different movement planes and have the ability to rapidly react and change direction to either create space and evade on attack or close space on defense.

The term "speed" can be defined as time taken to get from point A to point B. In sport the quicker we get from A to B is critical and determines the players impact on any game. If you are not in a position to influence the game you are effectively out of the game.

The key question we need to ask ourselves when designing speed and agility training sessions for rugby is where does A start and B finish? We know for track and field sprinting A is the start line and B is 100m away in a straight line. However during a rugby game there will be numerous starting points (A) and just as many varying finishing points (B). During the game a player may need to react and move quickly for as little as only two steps to the left to make a tackle on an attacking player attempting to sidestep past them on the inside. At another point in the game the same player may be forced to cover defend and chase down an opposition break requiring a straight line sprint of 40m.

The point being, short space explosive acceleration and multi-directional speed is critical in order to clear space in traffic or contact areas in front of the advantage line, before the need for straight line speed kicks in after the line has been broken and the attacker is past the advantage line and in space. At that time the support players and defenders must also utilise straight line speed to aid in the attack or get back to create a defensive line when the attack is halted by the next tackle.

Straight line speed is of great importance however if only straight line running is emphasised for speed development the physical skills needed to sidestep, move laterally, react to the game situation and evade contact or defenders are not developed.

Multidirectional speed and agility is dependant on a combination of 'speed skills'

Movement patterns and rugby speed skills include:
- Forward – Linear or straight line acceleration.
- Backwards - Backpedalling
- Lateral – Sideways speed
- Forwards to backwards change of direction
- Forwards to lateral change of direction
- Backwards to lateral change of direction
- Lateral to lateral change – Side to side change of direction
- Lateral to forwards change of direction
- Lateral to backwards change of direction
- Forwards to diagonal (sidestep or swerve at speed)

These specific movement patterns <u>can</u> be trained as a skill. Mastering them will allow players to have greater body control in any given situation and much improved first step quickness. First step quickness can be termed the ability of player to move explosively with balance in any direction off one step. As opposed to having to reduce speed, stop to regain body control, or taking 2-3 steps to initiate speed in another direction.

These multi-directional movements will have a much greater influence on success or failure in rugby as it is in agility where space is created or lost. Spending training time focusing only on straight line speed will not help with the ability to move quickly laterally, to make a tackle, turn and chase a ball chipped over your head, or sidestep past an opponent when attacking with the ball.

Consider these examples:

A midfield player with excellent maximal straight line speed but no agility or ability to sidestep at speed is an easy defensive target. He may be the fastest in his team over 100m but if he cannot sidestep or change direction at speed he has little chance of breaking the line as the defense is not chasing him from behind, they are in front of him and can easily close his space. A midfield back that has excellent agility and can sidestep sharply at speed has a far better chance of breaking the line and advancing the attack even if he has poor 100m speed as he is likely to pass the ball or get tackled 5-15m after making the initial break.

Or consider a prop who is standing flat footed ready to make a tackle on an opponent hitting the ball straight up at him, the prop may have spent training time working on straight line speed and made good improvements in that area but what happens when the attacker sidesteps to the left? The prop will have a split second to react and move quickly to the left moving laterally (sideways) to make the tackle. It may be as short as one step quickly to the left with balance so that he can tackle strongly from the front and stop momentum. In that scenario the distance from "A" to "B" is very short but getting there quickly is crucial to stop the attack. Without good footwork, balance and lateral drive speed the defending prop will not be able to make an effective tackle. The attacking player may burst past him and continue the attack or get far enough past his shoulder to ensure continued forward momentum as he is tackled side on and dragged down as opposed to front on and stopped or driven back. This will free up his arms to make a pass or at the very least he would land behind the defender and past the advantage line allowing his teammates to continue going forward.

This is an example of **_"real"_** multidirectional speed and agility that may not immediately come to mind when players and coaches look at their "speed training". Important defensive tackles or scoring opportunities come about through winners and losers in one on one athletic confrontations.

In summary, rugby defensive screens are based around having defenders marking all attacking "bodies" of the opposition. To breach good defensive screens individual attackers must be put into positions where they can get past individual defenders to get behind the screen. To evade the defender the attacker must move their body quickly into space by using multidirectional speed. A defender will not be beaten by an attacker who runs in straight line directly at the defender no matter how fast he can run a straight line.

Distances Run

Athletics sprints are carried out over 100 and 200m. This sprint may be completed in 10-30 seconds.

Rugby players sprint over varying distances not usually more than 5-15m at maximal effort before changing direction, making a tackle, hitting a ruck or the phase being ended by the referees whistle.

Maximal Speed vs. Acceleration

It is widely accepted that maximal speed maintenance is one of the training priorities for track sprinters. Track sprinters train to accelerate to maximal speed as soon as possible and then maintain that speed for as long as possible over the event. Limiting deceleration is a major training goal as all sprinters decelerate in the later part of 100m and 200m events. The most successful sprinters are those that can maintain maximal speed longer than their competitors.

It is also widely accepted that maximal speed maintenance and minimising deceleration over long distances (100m & 200m) is of lesser value to the sport of rugby. Maximal speed is generally reached after first going through an initial sprint acceleration phase of 30-50m. Given that the majority of straight line sprinting for rugby is carried out over 5-15m the need to target explosive acceleration as opposed to maximal speed becomes clear.

A rugby player who has excellent maximal speed but poor acceleration (time that it takes to reach max speed) is far less dangerous than a player with excellent acceleration but poor maximum speed. The reason being simply that the nature of rugby means players very rarely reach maximum speed during the game, short explosive bursts of acceleration are the dominant distances run.

Rugby requires many repeated bursts of explosive acceleration over short distances as opposed to one acceleration phase followed by a maximal speed phase and lastly a deceleration phase to complete a one off sprint event. So in terms of training application we should train for the distances sprinted during games and in rugby's case shorter distances should be the focus.

For example when applying to a training session, 10 short acceleration sprints of 10m will be more effective to rugby performance than one sprint of 100m. 10 short sprints train 10 specific explosive acceleration bursts as opposed to 100m where acceleration is trained only once. Also of prime consideration is the fact that players very rarely sprint 100m in a straight line at maximal effort during a game and thus training time should be spent improving game specific distances.

A final point to note is that you often see 100m sprinters power through the field over the last 30-40m of a race and it is not unusual to see the winner just pip the field at the finishing line. Many of the world's most successful sprinters are not the fastest men over 20m and 50m and do not lead the field from start to finish, however because the sprint is a 100m event they have time to reach their maximal speed and overtake the opposition that may be have superior acceleration but inferior maximal speed and speed maintenance over 100m.

Of course rugby sprints are usually over within 5-15m leaving no time for a player with superior maximal speed to use that skill on the field. Acceleration is the dominate requirement and is hugely important when considering rugby speed development.

Energy Systems Utilised

Athletes complete a one off maximal sprint lasting 10-30 seconds depending on the event (100m -200m) and running level. They are fully rested when starting the race and fully recover after the one off maximal effort. Athletes are able to complete training activities while fully recovered as they have a singular focus. This allows for a far more effective use of neural form based technique training.

Rugby players compete over 80 minutes with intermittent rest periods for stoppages. Players must access all energy systems to deal with the demands of the sport. They are most often fatigued when required to sprint at maximal effort as the game is continuous. Rugby players very rarely have the opportunity to carry out speed training sessions while fully rested as they have many other fitness and game areas to train, therefore a training focus on form based neural and plyometric training is impractical and less effective.

Individual vs. Group Training

Track and field athletes often have a coach close at hand to give individual or small group technique instruction. This allows technical flaws to be assessed and rectified through close contact with the coach who is a specialist in the dynamics and techniques of linear (straight line) speed mechanics.

Rugby players either train as individuals, with a partner or with a team / squad. The squad of 15-30 players will be instructed by the coach or fitness trainer as a group which makes personal tuition in terms of perfecting technique drills impractical and difficult to manage.

Mechanical form drills are most effective if trained with perfect technique and repetition is required to ingrain these patterns of movement. One coach or trainer cannot instruct or analyse each player or correct technique, in addition rugby players do not have the training time to commit solely to perfecting track form technique drills in order to gain great benefit.

Running at speed in a straight line is only one of many game requirements of the sport and training time is spread across a wide spectrum. There is not the time for continuous rehearsal of technique when you only have 2 or 3 hours of time each week and linear maximal speed is one piece of the rugby speed and quickness puzzle. Track and field sprinters have only one training and competition requirement; that is to run fast in a straight line and stop.

Boots vs. Track shoes

Rugby players play and train in boots with sprigs in-season or thick soled running shoes through summer training

Track athletes run in light shoes with spikes. Many training activities well suited to the track are unsuitable for players wearing boots and running shoes with thick cushioned heels as ground contact, balance, centre of gravity and mechanics are all affected.

Ground Conditions

Rugby is played on grass that may be long, short, hard, soft, muddy and undulating. This varying surface does not have the stability of an artificial sprinting track. This tends to lead to rugby running patterns being shorter in stride length and strongly foot-speed dominant. Players cannot achieve the same range of powerful hip extension or leg drive as the surface is less stable than an artificial track. Therefore less emphasis should be placed on the stride length and more emphasis on foot and leg speed for rapid acceleration.

Ball Carrying

Rugby will often require the player to sprint with ball in hand. Carrying the ball does affect balance and mechanics and is unique to the sport. Many track based drills require the use of good arm mechanics to balance the activity and maintain technique.

Of course rugby players will also be required to sprint without the ball for the most part as only one player carries the ball at any given time. Point being it is important that speed drills are completed with and without the rugby ball to balance the demands of the sport.

Body Position

Track sprinting places emphasis on "tall hips" once the sprinters have come out of the blocks and reached an upright body position. Sprinters run tall and upright with a relatively high centre of gravity to maximise linear speed and stride length.

Rugby players tend to play the game with a much lower centre of gravity in a forward lean. This is due to the balance and stability demands of the game. For example changing direction, passing the ball, scrummaging, tackling, entering contact situations, entering rucks and mauls. A player cannot change direction or enter a tackle situation with an upright body position and "tall" hips. In fact, in contact situations the lower to the ground the player is the better, as there is less leverage for the opposition to push the player back and up or stop forward momentum.

Body Type

Track and field sprinters are generally "born" sprinters and genetically well suited to the athletic event. They are predominantly fast twitch in muscle fibres and their lower levers (hips, legs) are mechanically speed efficient. Bodyweight tends to be lighter at 70-90kg.

Rugby players have a wide mix of genetic ability as the sport has many different physical demands due to positional specifics. Props are not built like wingers. Many players do not have the athleticism or the training history to cope well with high intensity track based speed drills and are therefore more susceptible to injury. This can be attributed to differences in flexibility, core stability, posture, predominate muscle fibre type and bodyweight. A 105kg rugby player has far greater load and stress placed on his back and lower limbs than a 70kg sprinter performing the same activity.

Training Options

Conditioning and speed training techniques have evolved greatly over recent years. There are now a huge range of options and specific training aids available to players and coaches that can achieve faster, better and more rugby specific results.

Training aids now allow you to target specific aspects of multidirectional speed development and gain greater results in less training time than conventional speed training. Players can now specifically train the physical skills that directly impact on field speed and agility rather than train in the same manner over and over again without a change of training stimulus or ability to overload.

The vastness of the speed and agility field means that the information in this book should not be treated as inclusive of all options available to you. The training activities and information written is designed to offer you many options to select from and equip you to continually vary your speed training stimulus. It is also based on the writer's successful experience with field based rugby specific multidirectional speed development.

One point of note is that speed should be developed all year round as it is a trainable skill that will improve with consistent work. Too many players and coaches wait until late pre-season before implementing a small speed component into their training schedule. Training gains will be limited by this approach. Much greater gains will be enjoyed if you incorporate speed based drills into your year round conditioning schedules.

Key Speed Components:

1. Speed Mechanics

2. Footwork / Footspeed

3. Resisted Sprinting

4. Assisted Sprinting

5. Short Space Evasion

6. Cone Based Agility Drills

7. Free Drills

Speed Mechanics

Coaches in sports such as golf, tennis, and swimming recognise the gains in performance that can be achieved through specifically targeting technique. An increase in bio-mechanical efficiency can lead to an increase in fluidity, speed and/or accuracy.

Developing changes in motor patterns does not happen in 2-3 weeks. It takes practice and persistence. Repetition by way of warm up is required to ingrain the skills so when you are physically and mentally fatigued your body only knows one way to move. To be fast we must master speed skills.

Greater efficiency = Increase in speed

This section looks at mechanical components of speed and how the ankle, knee, hip joints, and torso contribute to fast movement. The drills are designed to re-write and ingrain effective movement patterns and allow players to become sprint flexible. Speed attributes can be effectively enhanced with warm up routines that include these dynamic skipping drills.

Straight Line Skipping Drills

These series of drills have been used in the track and field coaching field for many years and are widely accepted as core technique patterns. Generally speaking the drills are designed to break down the mechanics of linear speed and improve sprinting "skills".

They are well suited for rugby warm up activities as they get you warm and get you fast to develop speed. Speed sessions should be all about moving quickly and continually challenging your body with speed habits.

This type of warm-up is beneficial towards conditioning the nervous system towards efficient movement, developing fast firing abilities of the muscles, and increasing a fluid range of motion. To be fast you must master speed skills. You cannot get fast by training slow.

It is important to again note that some knowledge in the area of technique development and application is better than none at all. You do not have to be an expert sprint coach to teach speed mechanics. An understanding of 3-4 key drills is more than enough in most training and coaching situations.

Linear drills will enhance speed through improving stride length and or stride frequency.

Stride Length X Stride Frequency = Linear Speed Ability

Key components are:

- Ankle Position
- Recovery technique – Effects stride frequency
- Leg Drive/Hip extension – Effects stride length.

1. Ankling

We are starting from the feet and working our way up. Speed starts with the feet as this is where ground contact occurs and improvements in foot ankle positioning and strength is the first step to increasing speed.

The stronger and more stable the ankle the less drop in the centre of gravity, the greater the stretch reflex and greater the following drive contraction.

Key points:

- Focus on short fast skips working off the ball of the foot in the toe up position.
- Heels off the ground.
- Short fast skips and low knee drive.
- Get off the ground as quickly as possible
- Have light feet

2. Butt kicks

The butt kick is a drill that improves the recovery speed of the leg. Increasing recovery speed will quicken the rate of leg turnover and improve speed. When the foot leaves the ground it must kick up towards the butt to shorten the length of the leg. The shorter the leg lever the quicker the recovery cycle.

This drill develops both the strength needed in the hamstrings to repeatedly bring the foot up in the recovery cycle and dynamic flexibility in the quadriceps that lessens the resistance and leads to a smoother action. If quadricepes are tight they can restrict knee flexion by opposing hamstring contraction. This slows leg recovery and causes additional hamstring fatigue. As hamstrings fatigue the ability to explosively extend the hip weakens and leads to a diminished drive and shorter stride length.

Key points:

- Keep your knees pointing down
- Flick your heels up to your butt in a running motion.
- Keep the knees together by imagining they are locked with a steel bar.
- Short steps.
- Fast action

3. Skip

Skipping is a combination of efficient ankle, knee and hip mechanics. When mastered this drill should be performed at maximal speed with minimal ground contact. The loading, recovering, driving and landing actions of sprinting are conditioned with rhythm and body control.

The focus is on strong drive and fast leg recovery and efficient movement. To encourage good leg recovery action imagine you have a steel bar between your knees and you must step up and over the bar with every step. This will help with knee drive and leg recovery speed.

Key points:

- Toe over knee
- Smooth circular motion
- When you lift one leg the other should be fully extended
- Drive elbows back vigorously
- Take short steps reaching with the knee, not the foot.
- Minimal ground contact

4. Arm Action

Your leg speed works in conjunction with your arm speed. If arm action is poor you will have problems with leg action and balance. The arms are the levers that balance the trunk and legs. Arm action can either work for you or against you and has a direct impact on speed potential. Arms and legs must work together with rhythm and co-ordination.

Arm action is an effort to snap the elbows back. This action creates an opposite but equal reaction of jolting the opposite knee up which assists with recovery speed. Arm action must be tidy to minimise side to side movements that can slow you down. Try to work on good arm action when completing your skipping drills and also apply powerful arm drive to all speed training workouts.

Key Points:

- Arms locked at right angles
- Straight line drive- not across your body
- Shoulders stable not rotating
- Thumbs pointed forward
- Hands close to pockets
- Drive hand back to the hip and forward to chin level.
- Relax hands
- Don't reach with the arms, concentrate on the drive back

Section Exercise Options – Select one workout option to include in a speed and agility session

Workout Option	Distance	Drills	Training Block Time	Rest Between Reps	Training Level
SL1	10m	1,2,3,4	5 Minutes	20-40 seconds	ALL
SL2	10m	1,2,3,4	10Minutes	20-40 seconds	ALL

Note:
- One rep is up and back to the 10m cone (20m total)
- Rest 20-40 seconds – Listen to your body.

Small Hurdle Drills – Stride development

30cm small hurdles are an excellent tool for developing and reinforcing recovery mechanics and agility. They can be included as part of a warm up, circuit station, or as a specific activity.

The hurdles provide a physical obstacle to step over which develops the toe up, heel up, knee up leg recovery skill. With consistent training you will develop the skills to maintain good recovery mechanics at high speed.

The distance between the hurdles depends to a degree on the age and size of runner. Use approximately two steps between each hurdle as a guide and make adjustments to suit your size. As with most skills a slow speed with good technique is mastered before increasing speed.

If you do not have hurdles available substitute them with 30cm high witches hat cones.

1. Dead Leg Run

Run along the outside of the hurdles stepping up and over with only the right leg. Once completed walk back and repeat using only the left leg.

Key points:

- Straight line drive - watch for the foot being brought around the side of the hurdle. This is an inefficient recovery action. When watching from the front you should see a straight drive with the foot hardly being seen.
- Make sure the supporting leg takes a very short step and is placed beside each hurdle. Landing forward or back of the hurdle affects the mechanics and reinforces poor technique.
- Concentrate on reaching up and tucking the foot under your butt.

2. Run Through

Progress to running through the hurdles placing one foot between each.

3. Double Foot Run

This drill doubles the number of steps performed for each run. Place two feet in-between each hurdle instead of one.

Key points:
- Watch out for the clip clop and jumping sound. The run should be smooth and even.

4. Run With Sprint Out

Run through the hurdles and sprint out 5-10m when reaching the end of the line. Emphasis is placed on an explosive take off. This is a good drill to use as a race and can be very competitive.

5. Lateral Run

Lateral movement power and agility can be developed with a lateral run through the hurdles. This is also an excellent conditioning and balance drill. Simply stand side on and run laterally through the hurdles.

Key points:
- Stay side on with shoulders square.
- Fast feet and fast hands.
- Swap sides with each repetition. i.e. lead with the left shoulder for first run, change to leading with the right shoulder for the second.

Section Exercise Options – Select one workout option to include in a speed and agility session

Workout Option	Reps	Drills	Sets	Rest Between Reps	Suited Training Level
H1	1	6	2	1-2 Minutes	ALL
H2	1,2	6	3	1-2 Minutes	ALL
H3	1,3,5	6	3	1-2 Minutes	INT
H4	1,3,4	4	4	1-2 Minutes	INT / ADV
H5	4,5	4	4	1-2 Minutes	INT / ADV

Note:
- Rest between repetitions is a slow walk back to the start of the hurdle/cone set.
- One repetition is a run through to the end of the hurdle/cone formation. ie. 6 repetitions is 6 times through the hurdles/cones.
- Where there is more than one exercise listed divide the number of sets between the exercises. For example H3 = 1 set of each exercise (1, 2, 3).
- Where the sets cannot be divided equally between exercises complete the exercise that you are weakest at.

Multi-directional Drills

When only straight line running is emphasised the muscles used to sidestep, move laterally, and react to others are not effectively conditioned. Multi-directional speed is dependant on the education of the hip and lateral muscles and developing the dynamic flexibility and strength needed to maintain body control and limb alignment at high speed.

The hip is a ball and socket joint that can is capable of far greater range of motion than the hip flexion (knee lift) and hip extension (leg drive or push) required for walking and running in a straight line. Internal rotation, external rotation and lateral drive are all key multi-directional patterns that are often ignored and tend to go untrained to the detriment of rugby performance.

These specific movement patterns can be broken down and taught and once mastered will allow you to have greater body control in any given situation and enable first step quickness. These multi-directional movements will have a much greater influence on success or failure in rugby as it is in agility where space is created or lost.

Developing a greater range of motion also develops significant protection from injury as no movement pattern will be outside trained flexibility levels.

Dynamic flexibility is important for fast, fluid, and smooth joint movement. Developing dynamic flexibility is the first step in developing the patterns of movement specific to rapid direction change and must be treated as, and coached as a teachable skill.

The following selection of drills will help develop the mechanical skills, firing patterns, and dynamic flexibility required to master the skill of high-speed direction change and agility. The drills are not an everyday movement and repetition is required to firstly develop the range of motion and secondly the fast firing abilities.

1. Carioca Run

The carioca run is excellent for developing fast flexible hips and body control.

Running sideways rotate the knee high across your body and follow with a high knee step behind your body using aggressive hip rotation.

Key points:
- Emphasis must be placed on reaching with the knee as this initiates the hip rotation.
- The shoulders are kept as square as possible as this isolates the hips and encourages a greater range of motion.
- High knee drive across your body followed by a high knee step behind. Rotate your hips.
- Swap sides with each repetition. i.e. lead with the left shoulder out and left shoulder coming back.
- Light and fast feet with minimal ground contact.

2. Cross Over Skip

The cross over skip develops the ability to explosively step across your body and sprint right or left. Being able to pivot into a first step sprint is excellent weapon to master and is a common movement on the rugby field. It also has a positive impact on your ability to sidestep at high speed.

Simply stand side on and skip on the spot to get rhythm. Powerfully rotate the outside knee up and across your body using hip rotation. Keep the shoulders square to target good rotation from the hip and not a pivot from the ground. Square up and repeat with the skipping motion.

The foot must come up and the toe should pass over the knee as it does with efficient straight line recovery. The shortened lever pivots faster and will be in a higher position to apply powerful drive forces which will allow for much better momentum with the first step.

Key points:

- Moving laterally rotate your hips and drive your knee across the body, square up.
- Make sure you lead with the knee, not the foot.
- Light fast feet.

3. Lateral skip

The lateral skip develops specific strength in the lateral drive muscles responsible for controlling side to side movement. The speed of any side to side or lateral movement is reliant on the efficiency of these muscle groups and how effectively they can be recruited. Greater lateral strength will have direct impact on side to side speed and high speed direction change.

Key points:

- Simply stand side on and skip on the spot.
- Drive off the outside leg to push sideways.
- Care must be taken to stay square and keep the feet from crossing over as that will place you in an unbalanced position. The feet must be kept apart to ensure you have a foot available to drive off.
- Look for triple extension through the ankle, knee, and hip as you would for straight line speed as it is the drive that controls the speed not the reaching of the foot.

4. Drop Step

This is an excellent drill for preventing soft tissue injury in the groin region. It develops functional range of motion in abduction and external rotation (lifting your leg up, out and around). This dropping back movement is a common pattern in rugby when you must quickly turn about. This may be to chase a ball chipped over your head, the opposition, or to drop back quickly to follow the passage of play.

The movement is characterised by skipping backwards, reaching up, out, and around with the knee. Maintain a forward lean (don't lean backwards) to maintain balance and the ability to quickly change direction.

Section Exercise Options – Select one workout option to include in a speed and agility session

Workout Option	Distance	Drills	Training Block	Rest Between Reps	Suited Training Level
MD1	10m	1,2,3,4	5 Minutes	20-40 seconds	ALL
MD2	10m	1,2,3,4	10Minutes	20-40 seconds	ALL

Note:
- One rep is up and back to the 10m cone (20m total)
- Rest 20-40 seconds – Listen to your body.

Footwork / Footspeed

Footspeed and correct foot placement are skills that must be targeted specifically in training as it is the feet that control your ability to stay balanced and move quickly. All the strength and power gained in the gym is wasted if your feet are out of control.

The feet must be educated to align your powerful leg driving limbs (ankle, knee, and hip) with your trunk and centre of gravity if you are to stay balanced and change direction at high speed. Your feet are the only contact point with the ground and they must be conditioned to ensure limb alignment can be maintained at high speeds to allow you to exert powerful ground forces and explosive drive with every step.

With regular training, footspeed will improve for the necessary short explosive bursts, sidestepping and multidirectional movements that are crucial in rugby. You must teach your legs and feet to adapt to extremely fast patterns of footwork by repeating specific foot skills and continually reloading the ankle. Repetition is required to ingrain movement patterns and progressively master foot control at high speeds.

The Footspeed Ladder is a widely used and very effective piece of training equipment that is ideal for footwork training. The layout of the ladder teaches a continuous loading, firing and reloading of the foot. The Ladder is also excellent as a functional rehabilitation tool for re-education after ankle and knee injuries. The pattern allows for controlled, repetitive movement patterns and light plyometrics to be accurately progressed.

If you do not have a Footspeed Ladder set up small cones in a straight line spaced 40cm apart (20 cones if possible otherwise as many as you have). This will give you the small 40cm area to complete the drills.

Key teaching points for all of the following drills are:

- Light feet are quick feet
- Work on the ball of the foot - watch for scuffing which indicates a toe down and inefficient ground contact.
- Start off slowly to gain rhythm and progress to maximal speed with all ladder drills once skill levels allow.
- Let your feet stay in control and keep your feet ahead of the body.

1. Run

- Place one foot in every square or over every cone and run through.
- Progress to a two foot run placing two feet in every square or between cones. This is more challenging and doubles the number of foot contacts per repetition. Make sure the leading foot is changed with each repetition. i.e. lead with the left then lead with the right.

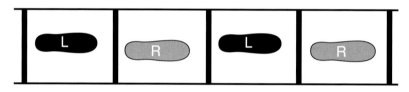

- Progress to passing and catching a ball.

2. Lateral Run

This drill specifically targets lateral movement footspeed. It has a direct carry over to rugby as players are often called upon to explosively react laterally with short step.

- Two feet are placed in each square or between cones and a side on posture is maintained with the shoulders staying square.
- Watch that the feet do not cross over and concentrate on driving with the outside leg.
- Change the way you are facing with each repetition change sides with each length of the ladder to develop both left and right side quickness.

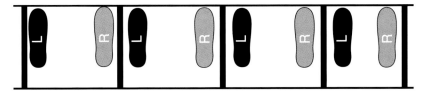

3. Forward Backward Run

This drill specifically targets the one foot direction change abilities in a forward and backward plane. It has a direct carry over to rugby as explosively reacting forwards or backwards are core movements. This drill increases the intensity of the ladder workout as it requires 4 foot placements per square, literally doubling the intensity on the previous series of drills.

- Try to get a 1,2,1,2 rhythm.
- Maintain forward lean.

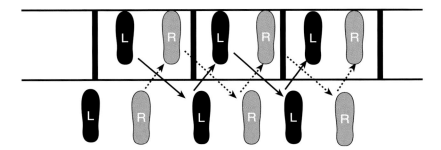

4. Sidestep Run

The sidestep run is a more complex drill and more difficult to master as the feet do not follow each other. This foot pattern targets a diagonal change of direction or sidestepping at speed. It is a two in one out pattern that must be mastered at slow speeds before progressing. Once mastered it is an excellent all round side stepping drill.

- A 1, 2 out 1, 2 out mental count is helpful for gaining early rhythm.
- Place cones in every second square as a progression for a larger range of movement.

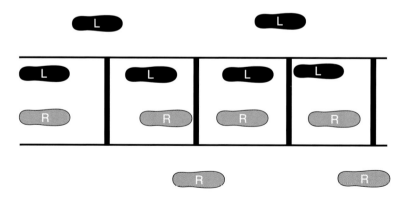

5. Agility Runs

Folding the ladder to make angles forms an excellent and very effective direction change agility course. It enables you to combine foot patterns and replicate specific first step direction change at high speed.

You can master:
1. Forwards to lateral change of direction
2. Lateral to forwards change of direction
3. Forwards to diagonal – sharp sidestep

- Angle the ladder by folding it over at right angles. Start with a 4, 8, 5 formation so that you have 4 rungs – fold – 8 rungs – fold and 5 rungs to finish.
- Option 1 - Run forwards to the first angle, laterally to the second angle and forwards to the end.
- Option 2 - Run laterally to the first angle, forwards to the second angle and lateral to the end.
- Option 3 – Run forwards all the way sidestepping sharply at the angles.
- Option 4 - Complete 1, 2, 3 with two steps in every square with the forward run.

Sample option 1

Note:
- Emphasis taking one step to change direction at the angles.
- Add sprint outs to a marker cone with any ladder drill for more complex workouts and greater intensity.
- Mix up the drills with ball and non ball carrying.

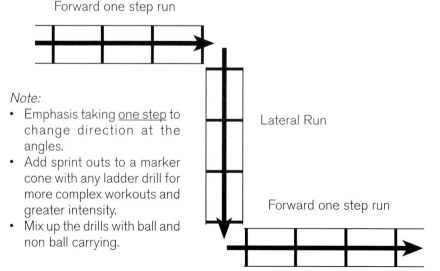

Forward one step run

Lateral Run

Forward one step run

Section Exercise Options – Select one workout option to include into a speed and agility session

Workout Option	Drills	Training Block	Rest Between Reps	Suited Training Level
L1	1,2	10 Minutes	20-40 seconds	BEG
L2	1,2,3,4	10 Minutes	20-40 seconds	INT / ADV
L3	5	15 Minutes	20-40 seconds	INT / ADV
L4	1,2,3,4,5	15 Minutes	20-40 seconds	INT / ADV

Note:
- Rest between repetitions is a slow walk back to the start of the ladder.
- Mix up the footwork patterns and continuously change the pattern over the training block.
- Focus on more complex drills as soon as you are able. Always challenge yourself for greater speed and footwork difficulty.
- Focus on your weak patterns where possible. For example if you are very poor at moving laterally to your left focus on your left side when completing lateral runs.
- Don't restrict yourself only to the patterns included in this book. There are many more patterns to master as you become more skilled. Talk to other players, coaches, trainers or look for video information to take your footwork further.

Resisted Sprinting

Speed strength is a term used to describe explosive power or acceleration training. Resisted sprinting is the most effective means of developing speed strength in the field with rugby players. Adding a load or dynamic resistance to your sprinting overloads your drive muscles and forces the nervous system to recruit greater "work" or power.

Fast twitch abilities are targeted and effectively conditioned to contract with greater speed and strength. This in turn improves your ground force production and corresponding explosive acceleration abilities as the strength or power of the drive (hip extension) determines stride length. This power is used for straight line speed but it also controls your ability to power out and change direction at high speed.

Resisted sprinting is also excellent for developing a stable core midsection and promoting a forward lean and low centre of gravity. This gives you much greater balance and stability that will improve your ability in stopping, rapid direction change and contact situations.

Common resisted sprinting techniques include the use of Power Speed Resistors, Speed Sleds and Speed Chutes. All are excellent training tools. However, this section of the book will focus on harness sprinting using Power Speed Resistors. Please note that Speed Chutes can be incorporated into all drills in this section and are particularly well suited to loading high speed direction change and Free Drills.

One person provides the load by holding back on the strap attached to the harness while the runner sprints at maximum effort. If you do not have access to a harness use a towel or jacket around the waist.

Please Note:

- Care must be taken to ensure the correct level of resistance is applied. Light to moderate resistance achieves greater gains. Do not hold your partner back so much that it negatively affects running style.
- This type of activity is very demanding and the distances covered, repetitions, and rest periods must initially be conservative and progressively overloaded.
- Obviously the type of drill, level of fitness, training experience, and stage of the year will influence the distances, rest periods and volume of weekly sessions. Generally speaking:
  - *Distances- 5-15m*
  - *Repetitions-4-8*
  - *Rest periods-1-3 minutes.*
  - *Volume 1-3 sessions each week*
- Rest periods should be long enough to ensure near full recovery between repetitions if speed development is to be maximised.

1. Resisted Skip

The skip is a low level introduction to speed strength development. Good posture and technique can be mastered before moving onto high-speed workouts.

Start with the feet together and lean forward so there is a reasonably straight line between ankle, knee, hip, shoulder and ear. Simply skip forward with the emphasis being placed on a strong drive, high knee, and short ground contact.

Note:
- 5 skipping workouts of 5-6 sets are recommended before progressing onto sprinting workouts.

2. Resisted Sprint

The sprint progresses the activity to maximal intensity. Maintaining short choppy strides is important to ensure the foot does not land in front of the centre of gravity, this maximizes the drive.

- Good body lean
- Powerful drive
- Aggressive arms
- High knee drive
- Maximum effort
- Triple extension

3. Resisted Sprint - Let Goes

A let go is when a loaded sprint is immediately followed by a free unresisted sprint. You are literally let go by your training partner. This is known as contrast training and the runner will experience a sensation of being shot out of a cannon when released from the load. Greater training gains are experienced when combining loaded with unloaded sprinting.

The partner holding you back calls "go" at a release point and you sprint unloaded to the finish point.

These drills allow longer distances to be sprinted and sports specific motions to be incorporated. For example a change of direction or a sporting skill such as hitting a tackle bag or picking up a ball can be carried out at maximum speed.

- 5-10m resisted sprinting followed by a release and 10-30m unloaded sprinting is recommended.

4. Lateral Run

Lateral speed strength is one of the most crucial and unfortunately most neglected aspects of a well-rounded quickness development programme. Too often linear speed is the focus and the athletic ability to apply lateral ground forces is not strengthened. This leads to a lesser ability to quickly move laterally, stop, and change direction at high speeds.

Lateral loading is the most effective drill to strengthen the muscles that will keep the hip stable and leg explosive. Collapsing at the hip and the inability to drive the body mass in a lateral direction with short ground contact and at speed is one of the most obvious weaknesses in rugby players.

For example, when performing a sidestep a tremendous amount of lateral strength is required to apply enough forces to drive the body at a different angle.

Any lateral weakness lengthens the ground contact time, collapses the hip and increases braking forces. This reduces drive ability when changing direction and leads to a slowing of speed.

Powerful players can change direction without a noticeable slowing of pace, this makes them a much harder defensive target. Players with untrained and poor lateral strength tend to slow down before changing direction as they do not have the stability and power to change direction and maintain explosive ground forces.

- The person holding onto the Resistor stands beside the runner and provides the resistance in the same way they did for the forward running drills.
- The runner faces side on.
- Start running on the spot to get rhythm then push and drive sideways.
- It is important that the feet do not cross over and good arm action is maintained.
- Focus on driving powerfully with the inside leg.
- Shoulders must stay square, as do the hips, as rotation will negate the benefits of the drill.
- Distances of 10-15m are recommended with a maximum of 3-4 repetitions on each side.
- Focus on your weaker side if you sidestep better off one foot than the other.

5. High Speed Direction Change – Side Steps and Swerves

It is strongly recommended that direction change at high speeds either as a sharp side step or swerve should quickly be incorporated into speed strength sessions. Direction change at rapid speeds must be practiced like any other skill if it is to be improved upon, and it can be dramatically improved with consistent effort.

The example cone set up on page 54 is designed to train for different side stepping or swerving patterns over varying running distances. The angle of the sidesteps and swerves and distances between cones should be regularly adjusted for maximal transfer onto the playing field.

For example a halfback will run much shorter distances than that of a winger. Halfbacks will generally be forced to sidestep within 2-3m after receiving or picking up the ball in an effort to find some space through the congested contact area that their position places them in.

Wingers run longer distances before changing direction, sidestep at higher speeds and at less angle so longer distances should be set up between cones. Wingers in particular should pay careful attention to their running patterns as their position (left or right side of the field) places them in a position on the field where they will sidestep and swerve in one direction more frequently than the other. Wingers do not often have the space to sidestep sharply on the outside of their opposition, they are also discouraged from getting to close to the sideline and risk losing possession so an inside sidestep is used most often. For example, right wingers will step more often off their right foot as this will cut back inside past defenders, left wingers predominantly step off their left foot to cut back into the field of play and find support.

<u>Note :</u> With any cone based agility drills stepping just before the cone replicates a sharp sidestep. Changing direction AFTER you run past the cone means you must run around it, this replicates a swerve. If you wish to target swerving then change direction after the cone and go around it.

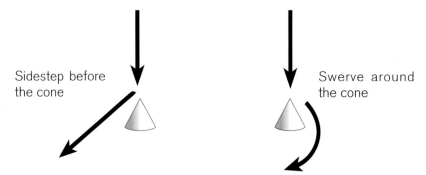

Sidestep before the cone

Swerve around the cone

Ensure you target any weak side with your side stepping patterns and don't become known as a player who can only sidestep well off one side. This will make you an easy defensive target for the opposition. If you are much better at stepping or swerving to the left spend more time with your training stepping to the right, so that you can choose which way to go to suit the game and space. The cone set up in this section is designed to allow you to balance both sides of the body.

Sidestepping and swerving are both important skills to train. Sidestepping is a sharp change of direction with a fast powerful step, whereas a swerve is a more gradual change of direction maintaining a greater speed. Generally speaking outside backs would use a swerve more often than others, especially on attack as they have the open space to use an inside outside swerve. Other positions will not often be in situation where they can use a swerve, so little training time if any should be spent on swerve style evasion.

However, it is important to note that all players by default use swerve techniques during the game when they may not have the ball in hand. Support running, cover defending, running to breakdowns and coming in behind the ball to hit a ruck, or to support a teammate with the ball in a tackle all require swerving as opposed to a sharp sidestep.

Note:
- Rest between repetitions is generally a slow walk back to the start cone. Listen to your body and take longer breaks if you are not recovering well.
- Where there is more than one exercise listed divide the number of sets between the exercises. For example PR4 = 2 sets of each exercise 3 and 4.
- Where the sets cannot be divided equally between exercises complete the exercise that you are weakest at.

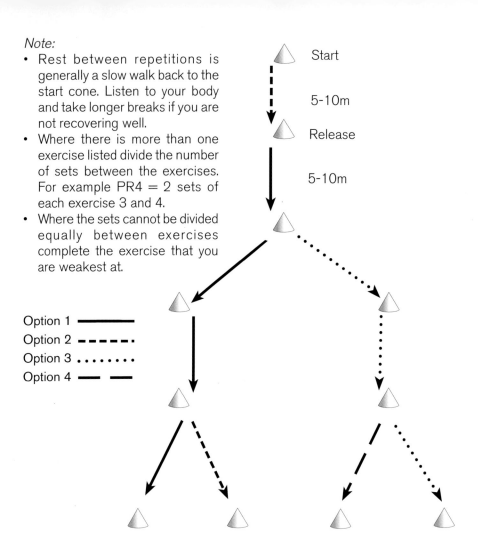

Option 1 ──────
Option 2 ── ── ──
Option 3 ●●●●●●●●
Option 4 ── ──

Section Exercise Options – Select one workout option to include in a speed and agility session

Workout Option	Drills	Repetitions in a Set	Total Sets	Rest Between Sets	Suited Training Level
PR 1	1	3	2	2-3 Minutes	BEG
PR 2	2	3-4	2	2-3 Minutes	INT
PR 3	3	3-4	2	2-3 Minutes	INT / ADV
PR 4	3,4	4	3	2-3 Minutes	INT / ADV
PR 5	4,5	4	3	2-3 Minutes	ADV

Assisted Sprinting

Overspeed is the term used to describe assisted sprinting techniques using an external device to force your body into faster sprinting speeds. The external assistance comes from stretched rubber flexicord that "pulls you along" as it contracts after starting in a lengthened or stretched position.

Overspeed training is excellent for improving leg speed and fast firing abilities. Improving leg speed will have a direct impact on improved running speed. It will also improve reactive strength which shortens ground contact time, another crucial factor in speed. Muscle memory means your body remembers the faster firing rate, which leads to an increase in unassisted explosive acceleration on the sports field.

Areas that overspeed training will improve:
1. **Leg speed/Stride rate** - The speed that you reload and recover your leg for the next stride. This is crucial to speed development.
2. **Technique** - Inefficient technique is made to feel awkward when sprinting at overspeed and poor habits are easily felt as you run.
3. **Confidence** - The confidence to burst through your speed barriers and feel what it is like to run "real" fast will give you greater confidence and speed when competing in your sport.
4. **Reactive Strength** - Because you are being pulled forward reactive strength or "more force in less time" is improved. This is excellent in limiting foot ground contact time. This lessens braking forces at ground contact and keeps you moving faster. World-class sprinters spend much less time on the ground with each step than slower sprinters.

Note: If you have access to overspeed devices the length of the flexicord system will determine set up so please refer to any training manual provided with the aid. If you do not have access to overspeed devices please follow the Free Drills sprint options later in this book.

The below information is based on a widely used 3m Overspeed model.

Set Up

- Connect the waist belt securely around your waist.
- Attach the flexicord to the D-Ring on your waist belt and turn the belt to place the D-Ring and rubber in front. Have your partner secure their belt and connect the flexicord to the rear.
- You stand on the starting marker and have your partner walk forward so that the flexicord is off the ground and semi parallel to the ground. This is your neutral position.

- Your partner (who is in front of you) then takes a number of steps forward which stretches the rubber. The greater the steps the greater the assistance and the faster you will run. 2-3 steps are recommended as a starting point. Never stretch the flexicord more than 5 steps.
- On your command both of you take off and sprint. Your partner will be "towing" you and as the rubber contracts you will be "pulled" along with overspeed. As you get close to your partner swerve to the left or right to avoid the flexicord as the slack will hang towards the ground as the tension is released.
- Your partner should slow down once past the end marker or when you overtake them.
- You will have to spend your first workout identifying the number of steps of stretch that is best for you. For example, if your partner places the flexicord under a 3 step load and you feel you are running too fast instruct them to start you from only 2 steps. As you gain experience with overspeed training you will be able to increase the stretch you are working with.

Note:
- Maximum of 4-6 repetitions per session.
- Full recovery between reps.
- Maximum of 2 sessions each week.
- Never complete overspeed if you are fatigued and always complete overspeed first in a training session.
- NOT SUITABLE FOR PLAYERS UNDER 16 YEARS OF AGE.
- DO NOT ATTEMPT OVERSPEED TRAINING BEFORE YOU HAVE COMPLETED AT LEAST 4 WEEKS OF FOUNDATION SPEED TRAINING..

1. Straight Overspeed Sprint 10m

Use above guidelines and complete straight overspeed sprint over 10m.

2. Straight Overspeed Sprint 20m

Use above guidelines and complete straight overspeed sprint over 20m.

3. Overspeed sprint with direction change

It is very beneficial to train specifically for high speed direction change if we are to master body control at top speed. Assisted sprinting when applied to the evasive running patterns for rugby becomes the most effective means of teaching high-speed direction change with control. Changing direction under these conditions has an excellent carryover to unassisted top speed sidestepping and swerving.

Note:

- Maximum sprint of 20m.
- Take off and side step or swerve at a 5 or 10m mark. Straighten up and continue through to the 20m mark.
- Make sure you work both right and left sides.
- Maximum of 6 repetitions per session.

Section Exercise Options – Select one workout option to include in a speed and agility session

Workout Option	Drills	Repetitions in a Workout	Rest Between Reps	Suited Training Level
AS1	1	4	2-3 Minutes*	ADV
AS2	2	4	2-3 Minutes*	ADV
AS3	1,2	4-6	2-3 Minutes*	ADV
AS4	3	4-6	2-3 Minutes*	ADV

Note:
- *Full recovery between repetitions.

Short Space Evasion

1. Live One on One Attacking and Defending

If you have a training partner there is excellent benefit in practising live one on one attack and defence drills. This is much more sports specific than training without opposition and is ideal to add in for late pre-reason and in-season sessions as it replicates game conditions and pressure.

Simply mark out a training area 20-30m square. One player practices being the attacker and the other the defender. The objective is for the attacker to score a try by beating the defender using explosive speed and direction change.

The defender must use the same skills to make the tackle and stop the attacker. Alternate between attacking and defending with each repetition and keep points for every try scored.

Note:
Mix up the starting distance and angle between attacker and defender for every repetition. For example:
- Attacker standing close to the defender (3-4m) or further back (10-20m)
- Starting on the left or right side of the grid as opposed to the middle for each rep. This applies to attacker and defender.

Other variations:
- Mix up the attackers starting and positional situation in ways that replicate the dynamic and unpredictable nature of a game.
- Vary the way the attacker receives the ball prior to starting the attack for every repetition. For example:
  - Standing with the ball rolling towards you.
  - Running to a rolling ball. To the left, right, behind, in front.
  - Catching a high ball.
  - Lying on the ground facing varying directions when starting.
  - Scooping a ball off the ground. From the left, right and varying distances

away from you. e.g You may run turn and run backwards 10m to scoop a ball and have to turn and immediately face the defender who is closing quickly in on you; leaving little space or time to quickly evade.

There are endless options to ensure each repetition can be different and continuously challenging to replicate game pressure.

Training Tip

The objective of the these drills is to replicate as many game situations as possible. Rugby is dynamic and unpredictable in distances run, angles, space available, positioning of defenders, and the speed of attacker and defender will be different for every time you have the ball in hand. You must train to react to what is happening around you and get to the level where all of the conditioning drills you have carried out in training can be applied to the actual game without conscious thought. The more instinctive you can become with your movement the better.

---

2. Evasion Belts

Evasion Belt training is a widely used and very effective means of developing short space explosive speed, agility and reactive speed in a fun, competitive environment. Short space quickness and reaction skills are targeted as an attacker tries to lose a defender and break a tear away connection between belts.

To lose a defender in rugby the attacker must move faster than the person marking them can respond. Most often it is the first 2 or 3 steps that will make the space needed to get involved in the game or be closed out of it. Conversely the defender must learn how to read, stay balanced, and react quickly to the movements of the attacker if they are to keep them out of the game.

With evasion belt training, the leader or attacker attempts to lose the defender using acceleration and agility skills. The defender must keep the belts intact. On a command the drill starts and each time the attacker breaks the belts he gains a point.

Try to get as many points as possible in a given time frame - 30 seconds is recommended. When the 30 seconds is up the players swap roles and the defender gets a chance to score points by being the attacker and vice versa. Scoring points ensures the participants work at 100% which is necessary if quickness gains are to be maximised.

Get away

Here the front runner tries to lose the back runner by using a combination of speed skills. They can accelerate forwards, change direction, stop, move laterally or use any motion to free up space.

- Explosive skills and sharp changes in direction must be emphasized. If players have not lost their marker within 6-8 steps they should stop and attempt to lose their chaser from a standing position. This encourages explosive and reactive skills.

Lateral Mirror

Players face each other with a slight hang in the belt. If it is taut it will come apart easily and defeat the nature of the drill. In this drill the leader attempts to lose the marker by using <u>lateral</u> movement only. Forward and backward movement is not allowed.

- Ensure that the players stay square and do not turn their hips or cross their feet over as this is inefficient movement. The feet must stay apart and players must face each other at all times.
- Emphasise remaining in the power position and remaining on the balls of the feet.

Section Exercise Options – Select one workout option to include in a speed and agility session

Workout Option	Drills	Repetitions in a Block	Rest Between Repetitions	Suited Training Level
E1	1	10-12	variable	ALL
E2	2	8	variable	ALL
E3	1,2	14-18	variable	INT / ADV

Note:
- Reps and sets determined by length of running patterns. Longer distances run will require longer rests so mix up rest periods as you do running pattern.
- It is generally recommended that the rest is a walk back to the start of the grid or swapping positions. i.e attacker becomes the defender and vice versa.
- It is beneficial to complete these specific game style evasion drills under some level of fatigue as this adds pressure and closely replicates game conditions.

Cone Based Agility Drills

1. 5 Cone Cross Formation

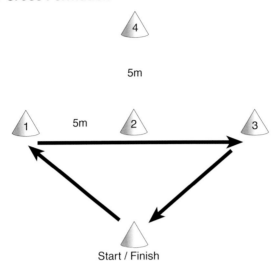

This simple cone set up can be used for any number of short space explosive acceleration and agility patterns. It will allow you to vary the direction of the running and corresponding agility demands with repetition. Just as each explosive run in a game will cover varying distances and running directions so should your speed and agility training be continually varied.

- Set up 5 cones 4-5 metres apart in a cross formation.
- As you look out from the start / finish cone number cones 1, 2 3 from left to right. The top cone is number 4.
- Plan a running pattern by selecting a sequence of numbered cones.
- Vary the running pattern for <u>every</u> repetition to develop well rounded agility and a challenging training environment.

Example running pattern 1

1, 3 finish.

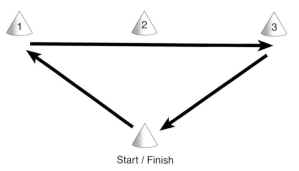

Example running pattern 2

2, 3, 4, 2, 1, finish

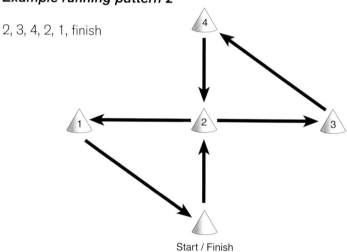

Example running pattern 3

1, finish, 2 finish, 3 finish

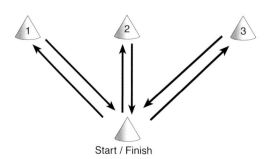

There are endless direction change and running distance variations to manipulate. There is also a huge range of skills to continually change at the cone point of direction change. You are not limited to simply running to the cone. Select from the below to change the skill for <u>every</u> repetition, this will keep your training challenging, fun and well rounded.

- Sidestep inside sharply at the cones
- Run around the cones with a swerve.
- Touch each cone with right hand
- Touch each cone with left hand
- Step off right side at every cone
- Step off left side at every cone.
- Drop down to the stomach and up again at every cone
- Vary the starting positions rather than using a standing start all the time.
  <u>For example:</u>
  - facing backwards
  - right side
  - left side knees
  - after a jump – jump and sprint
  - running on spot
  - running backwards two steps before accelerating
  - jogging two steps to the start cone before accelerating.
- Running forwards from start but always backwards to finish.
- With and without a ball, scooping a ball, catching a ball etc.
- Change the distance between cones. Make the grid larger or smaller.

2. Box Drills

By moving the position of two cones you can change the shape of the running circuit and nature of the movement patterns.

Options:

- Sprint around the cones clockwise.
- Sprint around the cones anti-clockwise.

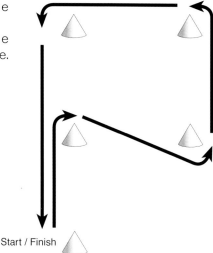

Start / Finish

Again vary the running pattern between each cone. Choose from forwards, backwards or side on lateral.

For example:

- Sprint forward to the first cone, lateral to the next cone, forwards to the next cone, lateral to the next cone and backwards to finish
- Forward to the far cone, lateral, backwards, lateral, backwards
- Lateral to the first cone, forward, lateral, backwards, lateral
- Lateral to the second cone, forward, lateral, backwards, lateral

Note: Use the same variation options as for drill 1 to make every sprint different.

Section Exercise Options – Select one workout option to include in a speed and agility session

Workout Option	Drills	Repetitions	Rest Between Repetitions	Suited Training Level
AD1	1	6	variable	ALL
AD2	1	10-12	variable	INT / ADV
AD3	2	10	variable	ALL
AD4	1,2	10-12	variable	INT / ADV

Note:

- Reps and sets will be determined by the length of running patterns and type of workout desired. Longer distances run will require longer rests so mix up rest periods as you do with the running pattern.
- Again it can be beneficial to complete these agility drills under some level of fatigue as there will be repeated speed training benefits.

Free Drills

1. Repeated Speed Endurance – Continuous Shuttles

This drill targets acceleration and repeated speed endurance.

- Mark out 10m and 20 m
- Sprint to the 10 m mark and gradually slow down and jog back to the start.
- Without stopping accelerate and sprint to the 20 m mark and gradually slow down and jog back to the start.
- Repeat this 4-5 x for a total of 8-10 sprints without stopping. This is one set.

2. Acceleration Sprints

This drill targets acceleration. and repeated speed endurance.

- Mark out a distance of 5m, 10m 15m 20m
- From a standing start sprint 5m
- Walk back slowly start sprint 10m
- Walk back slowly and repeat over 15m
- Walk back slowly and repeat over 20m. This totals one repetition.
- Vary the starting positions.

5m	10m	15m	20m
Start │	│	│	│

3. Get Ups

Get ups are an excellent drill for developing explosive acceleration. It is a competitive race between two players that ensures each sprint is completed at 100% effort.

- Mark out 5m and 10m

Option 1

- Start sitting on the ground back to back to your partner.
- One person gives the command to 'GO" and you get up and sprint to the 5m mark. The winner gains a point.
- Repeat over 10m.

Option 2

- Start with one partner lying face down on the 5m mark and the other on the start line.
- One person gives the command to 'GO".
- The back partner attempts to tag or tackle the front partner before he gets up and sprints past the 10m mark.
- If the chaser makes the tag he gains a point, if the front runner makes it to the 10m mark untagged he gets the point.

Note: If one partner is faster than the other and it is an uneven race; adjust the starting gap between you to ensure it is always a close competition.

4. Ball Drop

This drill targets explosive short space speed and reactive direction change. It is a very competitive drill which ensures 100% repeated effort.

- Mark out 5m.
- One person holds a rugby ball or tennis ball in each hand.
- The training partner stands on a line 5m away facing you.
- One ball is dropped and the sprinting player must accelerate forward and retrieve the ball on the first bounce.
- They return the ball to you and back peddle to the starting cone.
- Once he is set, drop the ball again. Vary between dropping the ball in right and left hands.
- Complete 10 repetitions with the running player getting a score out of 10 based on how many times he was able to catch the ball on the first bounce.
- Swap and repeat attempting to beat the score of your partner.

5. High Speed Direction Change – Side Steps and Swerves

Please see page 56 for cone formation and instruction. This resisted sprinting and contrast sidestepping and swerving formation is just as applicable without the resisted sprint at the start. It is a key drill that should be incorporated into your schedule with or without access to resisted sprinting training aids or a training partner.

Section Exercise Options – Select one workout option to include in a speed and agility session

Workout Option	Drills	Repetitions in a Set	Total Sets	Rest Between Sets	Suited Training Level
FD1	1	8-10	1-2	2-3 Minutes	ALL
FD2	2	2	1-2	2-3 Minutes	ALL
FD3	3	6	1-2	2-3 Minutes	ALL
FD4	4	10	1-2	2-3 Minutes	ALL
FD5	5	6	1		ALL

Speed and Agility Session Plans

It will quickly become obvious that off-season is the stage of the year where speed training gains can be most improved as you have more time available to commit to training. Pre-Season is also a period where speed and agility gains can be made however available training time is less. In-season speed and agility gains can also be achieved however the point being that if you wait until late pre-season or in-season before entering into your speed and agility development you will be limiting your improvement and playing performance.

One point of note is that speed should be developed all year round as it is a trainable skill that will improve with consistent work. Too many players and coaches wait until late pre-season before implementing a small speed component into their training schedule. Training gains will be limited by this approach. Much greater gains will be enjoyed if you incorporate speed based drills into your year round conditioning schedules.

Of course the number of sessions completed will vary greatly from individual to individual due to reasons outlined. You may well be capable of completing more than the listed maximum in-season, dependent on your situation. If you have time and limited team commitments then you can comfortably complete 2 sessions each week. Just make sure they are not both power sessions.

Three or four sessions each week for off-season and pre-season is recommended as the maximum as you must be fresh between workouts to recover, adapt and be able to train at 100% intensity at ALL times. Remember you CAN'T get fast by training slow!

Length of Sessions

Sessions can be as short as 15 minutes or as long as 50 minutes. If training time is short, do what you can. Perhaps get to training 20 minutes early and complete some ladder patterns. Aim for 30-50 minutes if training time is available.

The following tables give you guidelines on session plans to suit your current training level and position. Please refer to the session code as it relates to the speed and agility component. Simply go to the section in the book that includes the coded training block for workout details.

Where the table refers to choice (eg: PR4/FD2) it refers to training with or without a training partner. For example, if you do not have a training partner for a particular training day you cannot complete Power Speed Resistor, Overspeed, or Evasion Belt drills.

Where the table refers to ** this also means you have a choice of options depending on access to a training partner.

A Note on Warming Up for Speed

A warm up is built into every workout. DO NOT jog and stretch prior to beginning your speed workout. Jogging simply reduces training time, builds fatigue and is mechanically detrimental to speed development. When completing speed sessions have a total fast movement focus and WARM UP FOR SPEED!

As a general rule, speed mechanics and sometimes footspeed options will be the warm up component.

What and When?

Once you have passed the beginner level it is recommended that you arrange your speed training around **Power Days** and **Quickness Days**. This will enable you to work continuously on different parts of your rugby speed without over training.

Power Days -
Greater speed strength load
Quickness Days -
Unloaded footspeed, mechanics and agility focus

If you are managing to plan four speed and agility sessions into your pre-season training complete two Power days and two Quickness Days. This will ensure you build in recovery and adaptation time, and are able to complete all sessions with good energy levels.

Sample Session Outlines

Each training option table at the end of each section includes a column that indicates the difficulty or fitness level of the drill. Those levels being:

BEG	-	*Beginner*
INT	-	*Intermediate*
ADV	-	*Advanced*

Use the tables as a guide to the exercise level you should be completing. Progress to more difficult activities as you feel able. If you are a beginner and fitness levels are low do not complete any Resisted Sprinting until you have completed at least 9-10 foundation beginner sessions over 3-4 weeks.
Below is a selection of sample sessions plans. Each option is one speed and agility session structured in section modules.

Beginner - All Positions

Vary the options or design your own individual option sessions to suit training time and individual strengths and weaknesses.

Option 1

Training Type	Workout Option
Straight Line Skipping Drills	SL2
Multi-directional Drills	MD2
Small Hurdles Stride Development	H1
Footspeed	L1 Or L2
Resisted Sprinting	-
Short Space Evasion	-
Assisted Sprinting	-
Cone Based Agility Drills	-
Free Drills	FD1

Option 2

Training Type	Workout Option
Straight Line Skipping Drills	SL2
Multi-directional Drills	MD2
Small Hurdles Stride Development	H2
Footspeed	L1 or L2
Resisted Sprinting	-
Short Space Evasion	-
Assisted Sprinting	-
Cone Based Agility Drills	AD4
Free Drills	FD2

Option 3

Training Type	Workout Option
Straight Line Skipping Drills	SL2
Multi-directional Drills	MD2
Small Hurdles Stride Development	-
Footspeed	-
Resisted Sprinting	-
Short Space Evasion	E2
Assisted Sprinting	-
Cone Based Agility Drills	AD1 Or AD3 or AD4
Free Drills	FD1 and FD3 Or FD2

Intermediate - Tight Forwards

Option 1 – Power Day

Training Type	Workout Option
Straight Line Skipping Drills	SL1
Multi-directional Drills	-
Small Hurdles Stride Development	-
Footspeed	L4
Resisted Sprinting *	PR1 or PR3 / FD2 or FD 4
Short Space Evasion**	E2 or FD2
Assisted Sprinting	-
Cone Based Agility Drills	AD1 or AD3
Free Drills	-

* Complete PR option if you have a training partner. Complete FD option if you are training on your own.
** Complete E2 option if you have a training partner. If not FD2.

Option 2 – Quickness Day

Training Type	Workout Option
Straight Line Skipping Drills	-
Multi-directional Drills	MD2
Small Hurdles Stride Development	H3
Footspeed	L2
Resisted Sprinting	-
Short Space Evasion	-
Assisted Sprinting	-
Cone Based Agility Drills	-
Free Drills	FD2 Or FD4

Intermediate - Loose Forwards

Option 1 - Power Day

Training Type	Workout Option
Straight Line Skipping Drills	SL2
Multi-directional Drills	-
Small Hurdles Stride Development	H3
Footspeed	-
Resisted Sprinting*	PR1 or PR3 / FD2 or FD 4
Short Space Evasion**	E1 or FD2
Assisted Sprinting	-
Cone Based Agility Drills	AD1 or AD3
Free Drills	-

* Complete PR option if you have a training partner. Complete FD option if you are training on your own.
** Complete E1 option if you have a training partner. If not FD2.

Option 2 - Quickness Day

Training Type	Workout Option
Straight Line Skipping Drills	SL1
Multi-directional Drills	MD2
Small Hurdles Stride Development	-
Footspeed	L4
Resisted Sprinting	-
Short Space Evasion	-
Assisted Sprinting	-
Cone Based Agility Drills	-
Free Drills	FD1 & FD4

Intermediate - Backs

Option 1 - Power Day

Training Type	Workout Option
Straight Line Skipping Drills	SL1
Multi-directional Drills	MD1
Small Hurdles Stride Development	-
Footspeed	-
Resisted Sprinting*	PR4 or PR5 / FD5
Short Space Evasion**	E1 or AD1
Assisted Sprinting	-
Cone Based Agility Drills	-
Free Drills	-

*Complete PR option if you have a training partner. Complete FD option if you are training on your own.
** Complete E1 option if you have a training partner. If not AD1.

Option 2 - Quickness Day

Training Type	Workout Option
Straight Line Skipping Drills	SL1
Multi-directional Drills	MD1
Small Hurdles Stride Development	H5
Footspeed	L4
Resisted Sprinting	-
Short Space Evasion	-
Assisted Sprinting	-
Cone Based Agility Drills	AD2
Free Drills*	FD4 / FD1

* Complete FD4 option if you have a training partner. Complete FD1 option if you are training on your own.

Advanced - Tight Forwards

Option 1 - Power Day

Training Type	Workout Option
Straight Line Skipping Drills	SL1
Multi-directional Drills	MD1
Small Hurdles Stride Development	-
Footspeed	-
Resisted Sprinting*	PR4 / FD2 or FD4
Short Space Evasion**	E2 or AD1
Assisted Sprinting	-
Cone Based Agility Drills	-
Free Drills	-

* Complete PR option if you have a training partner. Complete FD option if you are training on your own.
** Complete E2 option if you have a training partner. If not AD1.

Option 2 - Quickness Day

Training Type	Workout Option
Straight Line Skipping Drills	-
Multi-directional Drills	MD2
Small Hurdles Stride Development	H3
Footspeed	L4
Resisted Sprinting	-
Short Space Evasion	-
Assisted Sprinting	-
Cone Based Agility Drills	AD3
Free Drills	-

Advanced – Loose Forwards

Option 1 - Power Day

Training Type	Workout Option
Straight Line Skipping Drills	SL2
Multi-directional Drills	-
Small Hurdles Stride Development	H3
Footspeed	-
Resisted Sprinting*	PR4 / FD2 or FD4
Short Space Evasion	-
Assisted Sprinting	-
Cone Based Agility Drills	AD4
Free Drills	-

* Complete PR option if you have a training partner. Complete FD option if you are training on your own.

Option 2 - Quickness Day

Training Type	Workout Option
Straight Line Skipping Drills	SL1
Multi-directional Drills	MD2
Small Hurdles Stride Development	-
Footspeed	L4
Resisted Sprinting	-
Short Space Evasion	-
Assisted Sprinting	-
Cone Based Agility Drills	-
Free Drills	FD1 & FD4

Advanced - Backs

Option 1 - Power Day

Training Type	Workout Option
Straight Line Skipping Drills	SL1
Multi-directional Drills	MD1
Small Hurdles Stride Development	-
Footspeed	-
Resisted Sprinting*	PR5 / FD5
Short Space Evasion**	E1 or AD3
Assisted Sprinting	-
Cone Based Agility Drills	-
Free Drills	-

* Complete PR option if you have a training partner. Complete FD option if you are training on your own.
** Complete E1 option if you have a training partner. If not AD3.

Option 2 - Quickness Day

Training Type	Workout Option
Straight Line Skipping Drills	-
Multi-directional Drills	-
Small Hurdles Stride Development	H5
Assisted Sprinting *	AS1 or 2 or 3 or 4 / or E1 or AD3
Footspeed	L4
Resisted Sprinting	-
Short Space Evasion	-
Cone Based Agility Drills	AD4
Free Drills	-

* Complete AS option if you have a training partner and equipment. Complete E1 or AD3 option if you are training on your own.

Gym Based Strength & Power Training

Weight Training For Strength and Function

The number of methods and patterns for weight training are vast. Many are grounded in the competitive world of bodybuilding and may not be ideal for sports performance. It is important to understand that resistance training programmes must be designed to enhance rugby performance, not just to build good looking muscles!

How a body sculptor, general fitness enthusiast and competitive sportsperson uses resistance training will be dramatically different as each has differing training goals.

The following table will help you understand how your weight training sessions should be programmed to match your individual training experience, stages of the season, and training goals.

Weight Training Tips

Key points to consider before engaging in any weight training programme:

- If there are any exercises you don't know in these programs ask a trainer at your gym. Don't try and guess them.
- Rotational stability including abdominal strength are important for both sport and everyday life.
- All traditional weight training exercises are only safe if they are performed properly with correct technique. Don't copy other people and assume they are doing it right. Ask someone who knows if you are not sure.
- Don't do a particular weights program simply because it works for the "big guy". Individual differences, genetics, training history and nutrition are just a few of the factors that will affect how you respond to a program.

Basic Rules of a Weight Training Programme

- Exercises progress from large muscle groups to small (e.g. squats before hamstring curls, bench press before triceps press-down, legs before upper body, chest before shoulders, back/chest/shoulders before arms)
- The number of reps per set will affect the training result (e.g. 8-12 for building muscle, 4-8 for building strength, 1-4 for building maximum strength)
- Most exercises have 3-6 sets. Occasionally more or less are appropriate.
- Most programs have 4-6 exercises.
- The body can be split into individual body parts (body building) or whole body or, whole body/upper body splits
- Weight training can be mixed with other training like cycling or can be performed in a circuit but mixing training modalities generally results in compromised results (e.g. a pump classes saves time but has lower results than a strength and aerobic session performed separately)

	Beginner/Lead In			Mass/Bulk			Strength		
	Off Season	Pre Season	In Season	Off Season	Pre Season	In Season	Off Season	Pre Season	In Season
Workouts each week	2-3	2-3	1-2	3-4	2-3	1-2	3-4	2-3	1-2
Sets	3-4	3-4	2-3	4-5	4-5	3-4	4-5	3-4	3-4
Reps	10-12	8-10	7-9	8-10	6-8	5-7	6-8	5-7	2-6
Rest	60sec	90sec	90sec	90sec	90sec	120sec	90sec	120sec	180sec
Number of Exercises	6-8	5-7	4-6	6-8	5-7	4-6	5-7	4-6	3-5

- Your strength program should be changed every 4-6 weeks to maintain a stimulus for strength gains. Variety is the spice (e.g. change bench press for dumbbell press every other week).
- As a general rule your movements should be controlled coming down and more aggressive going up.
- A muscle needs a minimum of 48 hours to recover from a weights session so bear this in mind when you put your training week together using the guide in the back section.

Key Strength Exercises for Rugby

This section includes photographic inserts of key strength exercises with technical instruction to follow for when you are performing each exercise. This guide may not be sufficient to guarantee correct technique (depending on your level of experience, injury status and flexibility to name a few variables) so please do ask a trainer at your gym for assistance with exercises that are new to you.

LEGS – Back Squat

Key Points:

- Feet shoulder width apart.
- Toes slightly kicked out.
- Idea of sitting down on something. Knees stay in line with the toes.
- Ideally back of legs parallel with ground (line between hip and knee joint parallel to ground)
- Chest high and back stabilized throughout the movement.
- Head up throughout the movement
- Maintain control of bar throughout movement.
- DON'T bounce at the bottom of the lift.

LEGS – Step Ups

Key Points:

- Top leg creates the drive. Left foot on box, right foot comes up to join it. Right foot returns to the ground. Left foot back to the ground.
- Change legs on the ground.
- The knee remains stable throughout the driving phase. i.e. in line with the toes
- Maintain the upper body in a straight and stable position to avoid the knee extending in front of the toes.
- Ensure box height means the knee is not higher than the hip.

LEGS – Split Squat/Lunge

Key Points:

- An exaggerated step forward while maintaining the body in an up right position.
- The front knee should not extend over the front toe.
- Once this position is attained the hips must drop straight towards the ground.
- The hips/pelvis should be under control at all times. Movement is up and down.
- Stop just before the back knee touches the ground.

LEGS – Good Morning

Key Points:

- Start with a slight bend at the knees and maintain the same knee joint ankle throughout the movement.
- Only continue as far as you can while maintaining good form.
- Chest high and core activated throughout the movement.
- Start with a light load or just bodyweight to ensure you get the correct technique.
- Only bend as far as you have control over you lower back and abs.
- NOTE – Once your lower back loses its natural curve, you have gone too far.

LEGS – Deadlift

Key Points:

- Maintain good core stability.
- Shoulders above hands and backside down at the start.
- Reverse the movement on the way back down.
- Feet shoulder width apart.
- Hands shoulder width apart. Palms can be facing the body or opposed (one each way).
- Maintain the natural curvature of the lower back throughout the movement i.e. the back remains relatively straight and stable.

CHEST – Flat/Incline Bench

Key Points:

- Feet are on the ground to stabilize. Medium width grip.
- Chest is high, shoulders and gluts are on the bench.
- Bar is lowered to the bottom of the chest.
- Bar is driven back to the start position in a slight arc.

CHEST – Flat/Incline DB Press

Key Points:

- Same set up as in the bench.
- Arms follow similar trajectory.
- Dumbbells drop to the armpit.
- Dumbbells are driven back to the start position.
- Ensure the dumbbells remain in a straight line.
- Chest is high, shoulders and gluts are on the bench.

BACK – Chin Ups

Key Points:

- Arms are straight at the bottom of the movement.
- Chin to the bar at the top of the movement.
- Vary grip size and width between underhand (image 1) and wide grip (image 2).
- Also use a towel or rugby jersey to focus on the importance of grip strength.

BACK – Bent over Row

Start

Finish

Key Points:

- Body position is important.
- Weight is only as heavy as you can stabilize.
- Use different grips and pulling angles.
- Note the angle between the upper and lower body.
- Feet shoulder width apart.
- Hands shoulder width apart. Palms can be facing the body or opposed (one each way).
- Maintain the natural curvature of the lower back throughout the movement i.e. the back remains relatively straight and stable.

BACK – One-Arm DB Walkover Row

Start

Finish

Key Points:

- Must be able to stabilize weight of body plus dumbbell.
- Chest high and back in a strong, stable position.
- Do NOT put the non-lifting arm on the opposite knee.
- Maintain the natural curvature of the lower back throughout the movement i.e. the back remains relatively straight and stable.
- Step over to next dumbbell. Ensure you are stable and setup before you attempt each lift.

BACK – Reverse Press Up / Swiss ball or Box

Key Points:

- Aim to contact the bar with the lower chest
- Ensure you do not use momentum to create the movement.
- Chest is high and body is rigid.
- Back and arms pull the chest towards the bar.
- Using a swiss ball increases the level of difficulty.

SHOULDERS – Split Stance Military Press

Key Points:

- Good stability through the core.
- Drive is with the shoulders and arms, not the legs.
- Legs are slightly wider than the hips and split front and back (5-15cm gap between feet).
- Hands are shoulder width.
- Bar starts at top of chest.
- Move head back as bar travels up.
- Finish position is above the head.

SHOULDERS – Split Stance (Dumbbell) Lateral Raise

Start

Key Points:

- Arm should finish just above 90 degrees.
- Dumbbells should be parallel to the floor (i.e. little finger is just above the thumb)
- Legs are slightly wider than the hips and split front and back (5-15cm gap between feet).
- Dumbbells start together in front of the body.
- Chest is held high and back is relatively straight and stable.

Finish

SHOULDERS – Seated DB Press

Start

Key Points:

- Dumbbells start at the outside points of the shoulders and travel above the head to the point where they meet.
- Ideally you should have your back unsupported.
- Back is stable and relatively straight.
- Movement is controlled at all times.
- Core is engaged to maintain a stable back position.

Please refer to the end of this chapter for a number of customized strength training programs.

Finish

Power Training for Transfer to the Field

Power exercises are strong movements that are performed at high speeds. Examples of power training include:

- **Olympic Lifting (power cleans/push press)**
- **Power Weights (power lunge/power step-ups/weighted squat jumps)**
- **Rugby Field Drills (Hit and Drive)**
- **Powerbag / Medicine Ball Throws**

Power training is very popular not only among elite athletes and serious trainers but also with fitness enthusiasts who aspire to challenge their bodies to perform feats of power and strength. Developing power will improve explosive speed, tackling, ruck and maul driving, scrummaging, jumping, kicking, passing and agility.

Power based exercises are highly beneficial but can also be highly technical and must be performed correctly in order to reduce the risk of injury. I recommend that to get the most out of this chapter you identify a personal trainer/fitness trainer who can take the time to teach you correct technique. When applied correctly these exercises will develop total body explosive power that will in turn positively impact on your rugby performance.

Key Power Exercises for Rugby

This section includes photographic inserts of these key power exercises with technique instruction. Again don't be afraid to ask a trainer at your gym for additional feedback. Technique is even more important for power based exercises where the movement speed makes correct movement critical to avoid injury.

Included in this section are two key Olympic Lifts that are a measure of strength and power. They are highly beneficial movements to master and incorporate into your training for the following reasons.

1. They involve the coordinated activation of a large amount of muscle mass in an explosive movement pattern.
2. They involve explosive extension of the body which can be seen in the scrum, cleanout, tackle, and lineout lifting and jumping.
3. While not being totally specific to all of the above movement patterns seen in rugby, they are closer than most of the more isolated movements that can be performed in the gym and have the advantage of being aggressive and explosive.

OLYMPIC LIFTS – Power Clean

- Start position is similar to the deadlift.
- Movement is broken into two parts.
- Maintain good core stability.
- Shoulders slightly forward of hands and butt down at the start.
- Feet shoulder width apart.
- Hands shoulder width apart. Palms facing the body.

- Maintain the natural curvature of the lower back throughout the movement (the back remains relatively straight and stable).
- The **first pull** is from the floor to the knees and is slightly slower than the second pull. This movement sets up the second pull.

- The **second pull** from the knees to the racking position is more explosive.
- Bar travels in a relatively straight line and stays close to the body.
- Explosive extension of body happens in a wave. Knees and hips straighten. Arms continue to pull the bar upwards. Lifter comes up onto toes. The shoulders

shrug and finally the arms start to bend with the elbows driven high.
- When the bar reaches the desired height you must acquire the "rack" position.
- At the point where the bar can travel no higher, the elbows are rotated under the bar. This drives the shoulders and chest upwards. The bar lands in the "racked" position sitting on the shoulders and upper chest.
- As the bar lands the knees bend to absorb the shock of the bar landing.
- The lifter then straightens to finish. To return the bar to the floor, lift it off the shoulders and catch it at the knee position Then return it to the floor.
- Maintain the natural curvature of the lower back throughout the movement (the back remains relatively straight and stable).

POWER WEIGHTS – Power Step Ups

- Top leg creates the drive with the knee remaining stable.
- The trailing leg powers up to be horizontal with the ground.
- Step back down and change legs on the ground.
- Upper body remains straight and stable.

POWER WEIGHTS – Power Lunge

- An exaggerated step forward as if stepping over a hole but wanting to step back.
- The front knee should not extend over the front toe.
- Power back to the start position.
- The hips/pelvis should be under control at all times.

HORIZONTAL POWER – Hit and Drive

- Hit and drive into a hit shield driving your partner back.
- Focus is on leg drive.
- Head is up. Body position is strong with the shoulders slightly above the hips.
- Arms are up and around the body or securing the ball away from the point of contact.

Strength & Power Training Application

Beginners Programme –

What is the aim?

The aim of the beginners workout is to introduce you to a relatively large number of exercises within one session so you get used to a variety of lifting patterns and movements. It is important at this stage that you learn the movement patterns correctly rather than trying to lift heavy weights.

You can use tempo (slower movement patterns with lighter weights) to help generate good patterns. It is from these base movements that other more complicated lifting patterns can be introduced as you become more experienced. The programmes have a balance of pushing and pulling movements, overhead lifting, and leg strength, plus core conditioning.

Mass/Bulk Programmes –

What is the aim?

Due to the physical nature of rugby, many players look to develop increases in muscle mass to cater for the demands of their position and the sport as a whole. A prop for example, may be trying to increase their body mass from 102kg to 110kg. Making this much muscle requires years of training, however it can be done.

It is important that this goal is not achieved at the expense of mobility so other types of training must be done concurrently with the mass/bulk workouts. Your nutrition is important in conjunction with these workouts and achieving this goal, so pay attention to what you eat and consider quality supplements to increase your chances of success.

Strength Programmes –

What is the aim?

Increasing strength is the result of a number of factors. Increasing the muscle mass can result in an increase in the ability to generate force. Another key factor is to use the existing muscle mass more effectively in the desired movement pattern.

Being strong in the gym does not directly relate to being stronger on the field however base strength work may help with injury prevention, feelings of confidence, increases in size, and with appropriate transfer training (e.g. power, plyometrics, speed-strength etc.) improved on-field performance.

These programmes are split into two and three day routines. In this way the same muscles are not overworked, have time to recover, and create variety in the training week. Again nutrition is important during the use of these programmes.

You will notice that the reps in each set are lower than the previous programmes. If you want to develop more maximal strength you need to lift heavier weight. Having a partner is very beneficial for motivation and safety with these routines.

Power Programmes –

What is the aim?

Once a pattern of strength has been developed, power routines can be brought into the equation. The key difference between strength and power programming is the speed of the movement patterns. Olympic lifting is a widely used form of training because it involves large amounts of muscle mass generating coordinated, explosive movements.

There are many other movement patterns that can be mimicked from rugby. Some obvious ones are scrummaging movements (e.g. one on one scrummaging), ripping in rucks and mauls (e.g. wrestling for swiss balls, medicine balls, and rugby balls), lifting in lineouts (e.g. lifting unstable loads above your head), tackling and mauling (e.g. hit and drive using a hit shield and a partner) to name a few.

All of these can be factored into your on-field power development. It is the goal of these power weights programmes to set you up for these patterns of transfer training.

BWB1

BEGINNERS WORKOUT (Whole Body Workout)

Warm Up – 6-8 MINUTES ROWING/SKIPPING

EXERCISE	SETS	REPS	WEIGHT	REPS	TEMPO	REST	GOAL
BACK SQUATS OR STEP UPS Superset with STANDING CALF RAISES	1 1 1 1 1 1	10 10 8 12 12 10			(2 : 1 : 2)	Spot partner as rest between sets (60-90 seconds)	Technique – ensure good depth and good control at bottom of the movement. Technique – looking for full range of movement.
FLAT BENCH PRESS	1 1 1	10 10 8			(2 : 1 : 2)	Rest between sets (60-90 seconds)	Technique – ensure good technique and good control of weight.
1-ARM ON BENCH DB ROW	1 1 1	10 10 8			Controlled	Rest between sets (60-90 seconds)	Technique – ensure good technique and good control of weight.
INCLINE DUMBBELL PRESS	1 1 1	10 10 8			(2 : 1 : 2)	Rest between sets (60-90 seconds)	Technique – ensure good technique and good control of weight.
REVERSE PRESS UP	1 1 1	10 10 8			Controlled	Rest between sets (60-90 seconds)	Technique – ensure good technique and good control of weight.
SEATED DB PRESS	1 1 1	10 10 8			(2 : 1 : 2)	Rest between sets (60-90 seconds)	Technique – ensure good technique and good control of weight.
4-POINT ABDOMINAL DRAW	2	10 X 10 SECOND HOLD			Controlled	10seconds on /off	Get correct start position. Maintain posture.
COMPLEX CRUNCH	2	20			Controlled		

Key points: Notice that the reps are reasonably high at around 8-10 per set. The movements are also controlled or have a tempo. This is a good way to ensure that technique is right before you start loading up as you approach the season.

M1A

MASS BUILDING / BULK WORKOUT (Whole Body Workout)

Warm Up – 6-8 MINUTES ROWING/SKIPPING

EXERCISE	SETS	REPS	WEIGHT	REPS	TEMPO	REST	GOAL
BACK SQUATS	1 1 1 1	10 10 8 8			(2 : 1 : 2)	Spot partner as rest between sets (60-90 seconds)	Technique – ensure good depth and good control at bottom of the movement.
Superset with							
STEP UPS	1 1 1	12 12 10					Technique – looking for full range of movement.
FLAT DUMBBELL/BENCH PRESS	1 1 1 1	10 10 8 8			(2 : 1 : 2)	Rest between sets (60-90 seconds)	Technique – ensure good technique and good control of weight.
BENT OVER ROW PRESS	1 1 1	10 10 8 8			Controlled	Rest between sets (60-90 seconds)	Technique – ensure good technique and good control of weight.
SEATED DB PRESS	1 1 1	10 10 8 8			(2 : 1 : 2)	Rest between sets (60-90 seconds)	Technique – ensure good technique and good control of weight.
LYING SIDE RAISE	2	12 (L & R)			Controlled		Ensure correct start position. Maintain posture.
SWISSBALL HIP LOWER	2	10			Controlled		

Key points: Notice that the reps are reasonably high at around 8-10 per set. The movements are also controlled or have a tempo. This is a good way to ensure that technique is right before you start loading up as you approach the season.

M2A

MASS/BULK WORKOUT (LEGS) (3-day split routine)

Warm Up – 6-8 MINUTES ROWING/SKIPPING

FORWARDS/BACKWARDS WALKING LUNGE (6F/6B X 2 SETS), FREE STEP UPS OR SQUATS (12 X 2)

EXERCISE	SETS	REPS	WEIGHT	REPS	TEMPO	REST	GOAL
BACK SQUATS	1 1 1 1 1	10 10 8 10 10			(2 : 1 : 2)	Complete Dumbbell Split Lunge as (60-90 seconds) super set	Technique – ensure good depth and good control at bottom of the movement.
Superset with							Technique – good control of pelvis. Good upper body posture.
DUMBBELL SPLIT LUNGE	1 1 1 1	5 4 4 5			(2 : x : 2)	Spot partner as rest between sets (60-90 seconds)	
BARBELL STEP UPS	1 1 1 1	10 10 10 8 8			Controlled	Complete Barbell (Good Morning as super set	Technique – top leg creates the drive. Stability about the knee. Change legs on the ground.
Superset with							
BARBELL GOOD MORNING	1 1 1 1	10 10 8 8			Controlled	Rest between sets (60-90 seconds)	Technique – good core set up. Maintain joint angle at knee.
Extra Option STANDING CALF RAISE	1 1	12 10			(2 : x : 2)	Rest between sets (60-90 seconds)	
LOWER ABS – HORSE STANCE	2	5 EACH LEG/ARM			Controlled	10SEC ON 10SEC OFF	Ensure correct start position. Maintain posture.

Key points: Notice that the reps are reasonably high at around 8-10 per set. The movements are also controlled or have a tempo. This is a good way to ensure that technique is right before you start loading up as you approach the season.

M2B

MASS/BULK WORKOUT (CHEST/SHOULDERS) (3-day split routine)

Warm Up - 6-8 MINUTES GRINDING/BOXING/SHADOW BOXING/SPEED BALL ETC.

EXERCISE	SETS	REPS	WEIGHT	REPS	TEMPO	REST	GOAL / LOAD
FLAT BENCH PRESS	1 1 1 1	10 10 8 8			(2 : 1 : 1)	Spot partner as rest between sets (60-90 seconds)	Technique – ensure good position on bench and good bar control.
INCLINE DB PRESS	1 1 1 1	1 8 8 6 6			(2 : 1 : 1)	Spot partner as rest between sets (60-90 seconds)	Technique – looking for good control of the dumbbells.
SEATED DB PRESS (UNSUPPORTED) Superset with	1 1 1	S 10 10 8 8			(2 : 1 : 1)	Complete Split stance Dumbbell Lateral Raise as super set	Technique – good set through core for stability. Lighter weight with good form. No back on bench.
SPLIT STANCE DUMBBELL LATERAL RAISE	1 1 1	10 10 10			Controlled	Rest between sets (60-90 seconds)	Technique – good core set up. Arms to 90 degrees. Dumbbells parallel to floor.
SWISS-BALL RUSSIAN TWIST	3	6 L/R			Controlled	(60-90 seconds)	Good core set up. Body parallel to ground.

M2C

MASS/BULK WORKOUT (BACK) (3-day split routine)

Warm Up – 4-6 MINUTES ROWING/SKIPPING , LIGHT LATERAL PULLDOWNS (2 X 10)

EXERCISE	SETS	REPS	WEIGHT	REPS	TEMPO	REST	GOAL / LOAD
CHIN UP/PULL UP (ALTERNATE REV CHIN AND WIDE GRIP FRONT CHIN)	1 1 1 1	Max Max of 8 Max of 8 Max of 6 Max.			(1 : x : 1)	Complete Swiss ball Reverse Press Up as super set	Technique – ensure good control. No more than 2 reps in the later sets. Change grip width and pattern.
Superset with							
SWISSBALL REVERSE PRESS UP	1 1 1	10 10 8 8			Controlled	Spot partner as rest between sets (90-120 seconds)	Technique – maintain strong core. Chest to bar are counted as full reps.
1-ARM ON BENCH DB ROW	1 1 1	10 10 8 8			(1 : x : 1)	Complete Tempo Deadlift as super set	Technique – good set through core for stability.
Superset with							
TEMPO DEADLIFT (TECHNIQUE 40-60kg)	1 (L/R) 1 (L/R) 1 (L/R) 1 (L/R)	10 10 9 9			(2 : 1 : 2)	Rest between sets (60-90 seconds)	Technique – good core set up.
MEDICINE BALL or POWERBAG WOODCHOP	2	6/6/6/6			Controlled	(60-90 seconds)	Good core setup. Going left and right, up and down.

M3A   MASS/BULK WORKOUT (LEGS/BACK/BICEPS) (2-day split routine)

Warm Up – 6-8 MINUTES ROWING/SKIPPING

EXERCISE	SETS	REPS	WEIGHT	REPS	TEMPO	REST	GOAL
BACK SQUAT OR DEADLIFTS	1 1 1 1	10 10 8 8			(2 : 1 : 2)	Spot partner as rest between sets (60-90 seconds)	Technique – ensure good depth and good control at bottom of movement.
STEP UPS	1 1 1	10 10 8			(2 : 1 : 2)	Rest between sets (60-90 seconds)	Technique – ensure good technique and good control of weight.
REVERSE GRIP FRONT CHIN OR WIDE GRIP FRONT CHIN	1 1 1 1	To Max. To Max. To Max. To Max.			Controlled	Rest between sets (60-90 seconds)	Technique – ensure good technique and good control of weight.
BENT OVER ROW	1 1 1 1	10 10 8 8			(2 : 1 : 2)	Rest between sets (60-90 seconds)	Technique – ensure good technique and good control of weight.
BARBELL CURLS	1 1 1	10 10 8			(2 : 1 : 2)	Rest between sets (60-90 seconds)	Technique – ensure good technique and good control of weight.
PRONE SWISS BALL LEG EXTENSION	1 1	10 10			(2 : 1 : 2)		Technique – ensure good technique and good control of weight.
MEDICINE BALL or POWERBAG WOODCHOPPER	2	10			Controlled		

Key points: Notice that the reps are reasonably high at around 8-10 per set. The movements are also controlled or have a tempo. This is a good way to ensure that technique is right before you start loading up as you approach the season.

M3B

MASS/BULK WORKOUT (CHEST/SHOULDERS/TRICEPS) (2-day split routine)

Warm Up – 6-8 MINUTES ROWING/SKIPPING

EXERCISE	SETS	REPS	WEIGHT	REPS	TEMPO	REST	GOAL
FLAT BENCH PRESS	1 1 1 1	10 10 8 8			(2 : 1 : 2)	Spot partner as rest between sets (60-90 seconds)	Technique – ensure good depth and good control at bottom of the movement.
INCLINE DB PRESS	1 1 1	10 8 8			(2 : 1 : 2)	Rest between sets (60-90 seconds)	Technique – ensure good technique and good control of weight.
SEATED DB PRESS	1 1 1 1	10 10 8 8			(2 : 1 : 2)	Rest between sets (60-90 seconds)	Technique – ensure good technique and good control of weight.
SPLIT-STANCE LATERAL RAISE	1 1 1	10 10 8			(2 : 1 : 2)	Rest between sets (60-90 seconds)	Technique – ensure good technique and good control of weight.
TRICEP PRESSDOWN	1 1 1	10 10 8			(2 : 1 : 2)	Rest between sets (60-90 seconds)	Technique – ensure good technique and good control of weight.
SWISSBALL OBLIQUE SIDE RAISE	2	4 (L/MID/R)			Controlled		Get correct start position. Maintain posture.
SWISSBALL BEARHUG	2	4 (L/R)			3-4 sec hold each side		

S1A

STRENGTH WORKOUT (LEGS) (3-day split routine)
Warm Up – 6-8 MINUTES ROWING/SKIPPING

FORWARDS/BACKWARDS WALKING LUNGE (6F/6B X 2 SETS), FREE STEP UPS OR SQUATS (12 X 2)

EXERCISE	SETS	REPS	WEIGHT	REPS	TEMPO	REST	GOAL
BACK SQUATS	1 1 1 1	8 8 6 6 4			(2 : x : 1)	Complete Dumbbell rest between sets (Split Lunge as super set)	Technique – ensure good depth and good control at bottom of the movement.
Superset with							
DUMBBELL SPLIT LUNGE	1 1 1 1	4 3 3 4			· (1 : x : 1)	Rest between sets (90-120 seconds)	Technique – good control of pelvis. Good upper body posture.
DEADLIFT	1 1 1 1	8 6 6 4			Controlled	Rest between sets (90-120 seconds)	Technique –good control of pelvis. Good upper body posture.
BARBELL STEP UPS	1 1 1 1	8 6 6 4			Controlled	Rest between sets (90-120 seconds)	Technique – top leg creates the drive. Stability about the knee. Change legs on the ground.
Extra Option STANDING CALF RAISE	1 1 1	12 10 8			(2 : x : 1)	Rest between sets (60-90 seconds)	
LOWER ABS – HORSE STANCE	2	5 EACH LEG/ARM			Controlled	10SEC ON 10SEC OFF	Get correct start position. Maintain posture.

Key points: Notice that the reps have dropped to between 4 and 8 per set. The movements still have controlled down movements but have aggressive positive (up) movements. This is a good way to ensure that you are used to higher loads as you adjust to more power based movements.

S1B

STRENGTH WORKOUT (CHEST/SHOULDERS) (3-day split routine)
Warm Up - 6-8 MINUTES GRINDING/BOXING/BOXING/SHADOW BOXING/SPEED BALL ETC.

EXERCISE	SETS	REPS	WEIGHT	REPS	TEMPO	REST	GOAL / LOAD
FLAT BENCH PRESS	1 1 1 1	8 8 8 6			(2 : 0 : x)	Spot partner as rest between sets (60-90 seconds)	Technique – ensure good position on bench and good bar control.
Superset with							
MEDICINE BALL or POWERBAG CHEST THROW (2 ARM)	1 1 1 1	8 8 6 6			Explosive		Explosive acceleration of the bar. Good core control.
INCLINE DB PRESS	1 1 1 1	7 7 6 6			(2 : 0 : x)	Spot partner as rest between sets (60-90 seconds)	Technique – looking for good control of the dumbbells.
SPLIT STANCE MILITARY PRESS	1 1 1 1	8 8 6 6			(2 : x : 1)	Complete Split Stance (Dumbbell Lateral Raise as super set)	Technique – good set through core for stability. Lighter weight with good form.
Superset with							
SPLIT STANCE DUMBBELL LATERAL RAISE	1 1 1	10 8 8			Controlled	Rest between sets (60-90 seconds)	Technique – good core set up. Arms to 90 degrees. Dumbbells parallel to floor.
SWISS-BALL RUSSIAN TWIST	3	6 L/R			Controlled	(60-90 seconds)	Good core set up. Hips parallel.

S1C

STRENGTH WORKOUT (BACK) (3-day split routine)

Warm Up - 4-6 MINUTES ROWING/SKIPPING

LIGHT LATPULLDOWNS (2 X 10)

EXERCISE	SETS	REPS	WEIGHT	REPS	TEMPO	REST	GOAL / LOAD
CHIN UP/PULL UP (WEIGHTED) (ALTERNATE REV CHIN AND WIDE GRIP FRONT CHIN)	1 1 1 1 1	Max. Max of 8 Max of 6 Max of 4 Max.			Controlled	Spot partner as rest between sets (90-120 seconds)	Technique – ensure good control. No more than 2 reps in the later sets. Change grip width and pattern. No leg swing.
BARBELL BENT-OVER-ROW	1 1 1 1	10 9 9 8 8			(1 : x : 1)	Rest between sets (60-90 seconds)	Technique – good set through core for stability.
1-ARM ON BENCH DB ROW	1 (L/R) 1 (L/R) 1 (L/R) 1 (L/R)	8 8 6 6			Controlled	Rest between sets (60-90 seconds)	Good stable setup. Don't use momentum in movement.
SWISS-BALL BEARHUGS	2	6 L/R			(2 : 1 : 2)	Rest between sets (60-90 seconds)	Good core setup. Going left and right, up and down.

S2A

STRENGTH WORKOUT (LEGS/BACK/BICEPS) (2-day split routine)
Warm Up – 6-8 MINUTES ROWING/SKIPPING

EXERCISE	SETS	REPS	WEIGHT	REPS	TEMPO	REST	GOAL
BACK SQUAT OR DEADLIFTS	1 1 1 1	8 8 6 4			(2 : 1 : 2)	Spot partner as rest between sets (60-90 seconds)	Technique – ensure good depth and good control at bottom of the movement.
STEP UPS	1 1 1	8 6 8			(2 : 1 : 2)	Rest between sets (60-90 seconds)	Technique –ensure good technique and good control of weight.
REVERSE GRIP FRONT CHIN OR WIDE GRIP FRONT CHIN (WEIGHTED)	1 1 1 1	Max. of 6 Max. of 6 Max. of 4 To Max.			Controlled	Rest between sets (60-90 seconds)	Technique – ensure good technique and good control of weight.
BENT OVER ROW	1 1 1 1	8 8 6 6			(2 : 1 : 2)	Rest between sets (60-90 seconds)	Technique – ensure good technique and good control of weight.
SEATED ALTERNATE DUMBBELL CURLS	1 1 1	8 (L/R) 6 (L/R) 6 (L/R)			(2 : 1 : 2)	Rest between sets (60-90 seconds)	Technique – ensure good technique and good control of weight.
SUPINE TABLE TOP BALANCE	1 1	6 (L/R) 6 (L/R)			(2 : 1 : 2)	Rest between sets (60-90 seconds)	Technique –ensure good technique and good control of weight.
STANDING CABLE PULLDOWN	2	4 (L/MID/R)			Controlled		Get correct start position. Maintain posture.
MEDICINE BALL or POWERBAG WOODCHOPPER	2	10			Controlled		

Key points: Notice that the reps are reasonably high at around 8-10 per set. The movements are also controlled or have a tempo. This is a good way to ensure that technique is right before you start loading up as you approach the season.

S2B

STRENGTH WORKOUT (CHEST/SHOULDERS/TRICEPS) (2-day split routine)

Warm Up – 6-8 MINUTES ROWING/SKIPPING

EXERCISE	SETS	REPS	WEIGHT	REPS	TEMPO	REST	GOAL
FLAT BENCH PRESS	1 1 1 1	8 6 6 4			(2 : 1 : 2)	Spot partner as rest between sets (60-90 seconds)	Technique – ensure good depth and good control at bottom of the movement.
INCLINE DB PRESS	1 1 1	8 6 4			(2 : 1 : 2)	Rest between sets (60-90 seconds)	Technique – ensure good technique and good control of weight.
STANDING MILITARY PRESS	1 1 1 1	8 6 6 4			(2 : 1 : 2)	Rest between sets (60-90 seconds)	Technique – ensure good technique and good control of weight.
SPLIT-STANCE LATERAL RAISE	1 1 1	10 8 8			(2 : 1 : 2)	Rest between sets (60-90 seconds)	Technique – ensure good technique and good control of weight.
TRICEP PRESSDOWN	1 1 1	8 8 8			(2 : 1 : 2)	Rest between sets (60-90 seconds)	Technique – ensure good technique and good control of weight.
SWISSBALL OBLIQUE SIDE RAISE	2	4 (L/MID/R)			Controlled		Get correct start position. Maintain posture.
SWISSBALL BEARHUG	2	4 (L/R)			3-4 SEC HOLD EACH SIDE		

PS1A

POWER STRENGTH WORKOUT (WHOLE BODY) (2-Day Split Routine)

Warm Up – 6-8 MINUTES ROWING/SKIPPING
GOOD MORNING (WITH BAR) (10 X 2), SWISSBALL SUPERMAN (8 X 2)

EXERCISE	SETS	REPS	WEIGHT	REPS	TEMPO	REST	GOAL
HANG CLEAN	1 1 1 1 1	8 6 6 4 4			Explosive	Rest between sets (120-180 seconds)	Technique – explosive bar speed with good control of core stability.
POWER CLEAN	1 1 1 1 1	6 4 4 3 3			Explosive	Rest between sets (120-180 seconds)	Technique – explosive bar speed with good control of core stability.
POWER STEP UPS	1 1 1 1	6 (L/R) 6 (L/R) 4 (L/R) 4 (L/R)			(2 : 0 : x)	Complete Barbell Power Lunge as super set	Technique – ensure good depth and good control at bottom of movement.
Superset with BARBELL POWER LUNGE	1 1 1 1	4 (L/R) 4 (L/R) 3 (L/R) 3 (L/R)			(2 : 0 : x)	Spot partner as rest between sets (60-90 seconds)	Technique – looking for good position on bench and good bar control.
SWISS BALL OBLIQUE SIDE RAISE	1 1	8 (L/R) 8 (L/R)			Controlled	Rest between sets (60 seconds)	Get correct start position. Bottom leg forward.

PS1B

POWER STRENGTH WORKOUT (UPPER BODY) (2-day split routine)

Warm Up – 6-8 MINUTES ROWING/SKIPPING

EXERCISE	SETS	REPS	WEIGHT	REPS	TEMPO	REST	GOAL
FLAT BENCH PRESS	1 1 1 1	8 6 4 4			2 : 1 : 2	Spot partner as rest between sets (60-90 seconds)	Technique – ensure good depth and good control at bottom of the movement.
Superset with							
SWISSBALL REVERSE PRESSUP (FAST)	1 1 1	8 8 8					
ONE-ARM WALKOVER DUMBBELL ROW	1 1 1	5 (L/R) 5 (L/R) 4 (L/R)			(2 : 1 : 2)	Rest between sets (60-90 seconds)	Technique – ensure good technique and good control of weight.
Superset with							
BENCH POWER PUSH OFF	1 1 1	8 8 8					
SPLIT-STANCE LATERAL RAISE	1 1 1	10 8 8			(2 : 1 : 2)	Rest between sets (60-90 seconds)	Technique – ensure good technique and good control of weight.
Superset with							
SWISS BALL MEDICINE BALL RUSSIAN TWIST	1 1 1	4 (L/R) 4 (L/R) 4 (L/R)					
MEDICINE BALL or POWERBAG WOODCHOPPER (ASCENDING/DECENDING)	2	8/8 (L/R)			Controlled		Get correct start position. Maintain posture.
SWISSBALL WRESTLE (PARTNER)	2	30 SEC					

ES3A

WHOLE BODY LEG STRENGTH (Early Pre-Season)

Warm Up – 6-8 MINUTES ROWING/SKIPPING

FORWARDS/BACKWARDS WALKING LUNGE (6F/6B X 2 SETS), FREE STEP UPS OR SQUATS (12 X 2)

EXERCISE	SETS	REPS	WEIGHT	REPS	TEMPO	REST	GOAL
BACK SQUATS	1 1 1 1 1	10 10 8 10 10			2 : 1 : 2	Complete Dumbbell Split Lunge as super set	Technique – ensure good depth and good control at bottom of movement.
Superset with							
DUMBBELL SPLIT LUNGE	1 1 1 1	5 4 4 5			(2 : x : 2)	Spot partner as rest between sets (60-90 seconds)	Technique – good control of pelvis. Good upper body posture.
BARBELL STEP UPS	1 1 1 1 1	12 10 10 8 8			Controlled	Complete Barbell Good Morning as super set	Technique – top leg creates the drive. Stability about the knee. Change legs on the ground.
Superset with							
BARBELL GOOD MORNING	1 1 1 1	10 10 8 8			Controlled	Rest between sets (60-90 seconds)	Technique – good core set up. Maintain joint angle at knee.
Extra Option STANDING CALF RAISE	1 1	12 10			(2 : x : 2)	Rest between sets (60-90 seconds)	
LOWER ABS – HORSE STANCE	2	5 EACH LEG/ARM			Controlled	10SEC ON/ 10SEC OFF	Get correct start position. Maintain posture.

Key points: Notice that the reps are reasonably high at around 8-10 per set. The movements are also controlled or have a tempo. This is a good way to ensure that technique is right before you start loading up as you approach the season.

ES3B

UPPER BODY STRENGTH (CHEST/SHOULDERS) (Early Pre-Season)

Warm Up - 6-8 MINUTES GRINDING/BOXING/SHADOW BOXING/SPEED BALL ETC.

EXERCISE	SETS	REPS	WEIGHT	REPS	TEMPO	REST	GOAL / LOAD
FLAT BENCH PRESS	1 1 1 1	10 10 8 8			(2 : 1 : 1)	Spot partner as rest between sets (60-90 seconds)	Technique – ensure good position on bench and good bar control.
INCLINE DB PRESS	1 1 1 1	8 8 6 6			(2 : 1 : 1)	Spot partner as rest between sets (60-90 seconds)	Technique – looking for good control of the dumbbells.
SEATED DB PRESS (UNSUPPORTED) Superset with	1 1 1	10 10 8 8			(2 : 1 : 1)	Complete Split stance Dumbbell Lateral Raise as super set	Technique – Good set through core for stability. Lighter weight with good form. No back on bench.
SPLIT STANCE DUMBBELL LATERAL RAISE	1 1 1	10 10 10			Controlled	Rest between sets (60-90 seconds)	Technique – good core set up. Arms to 90 degrees. Dumbbells parallel to floor.
SWISS-BALL RUSSIAN TWIST	3	6 L/R			Controlled	Rest between sets 60-90 seconds	Good core set up. Body parallel to ground.

ES3C

UPPER BODY STRENGTH (BACK) (Early Pre-Season)

Warm Up - 4-6 MINUTES ROWING/SKIPPING

LIGHT LATPULLDOWNS (2 X 10)

EXERCISE	SETS	REPS	WEIGHT	REPS	TEMPO	REST	GOAL / LOAD
CHIN UP/PULL UP (ALTERNATE REV CHIN AND WIDE GRIP FRONT CHIN)	1 1 1 1	Max. Max of 8 Max of 8 Max of 6 Max.			(1 : x : 1)	Complete Swiss ball Reverse Press Up as super set	Technique – ensure good control. No more than 2 reps in the later sets. Change grip width and pattern.
Superset with							
SWISSBALL REVERSE PRESS UP	1 1 1 1	10 10 8 8			Controlled	Spot partner as rest between sets (90-120 seconds)	Technique – maintain strong core. Chest to bar are counted as full reps.
1-ARM ON BENCH DB ROW	1 (L/R) 1 (L/R) 1 (L/R) 1 (L/R)	10 10 9 9			(1 : x : 1)	Complete Tempo Deadlift as super set	Technique – good set through core for stability.
Superset with							
TEMPO DEADLIFT (TECHNIQUE 40-60kg)	1 1 1	10 10 8 8			(2 : 1 : 2)	Rest between sets (60-90 seconds)	Technique – Good core set up.
MEDICINE BALL / POWERBAG WOODCHOP	2	6/6/6/6			Controlled	Rest between sets 60-90 seconds	Good core setup. Going left and right, up and down.

LS4A

WHOLE BODY LEG STRENGTH (Late Pre-Season)

Warm Up – 6-8 MINUTES ROWING/SKIPPING

FORWARDS/BACKWARDS WALKING LUNGE (6F/6B X 2 SETS), FREE STEP UPS OR SQUATS (12 X 2)

EXERCISE	SETS	REPS	WEIGHT	REPS	TEMPO	REST	GOAL
BACK SQUATS	1 1 1 1 1	8 8 8 6 6			(2 : x : 1)	Complete Dumbbell Split Lunge as super set	Technique – ensure good depth and good control at bottom of movement.
Superset with							
DUMBBELL SPLIT LUNGE	1 1 1 1	4 3 3 4			(1 : x : 1)	Spot partner as rest between sets (60-90 seconds)	Technique – good control of pelvis. Good upper body posture.
BARBELL STEP UPS	1 1 1 1 1	8 8 6 6 6			Controlled	Complete Barbell Good Morning as super set	Technique – top leg creates the drive. Stability about the knee. Change legs on the ground.
Superset with							
BARBELL GOOD MORNING	1 1 1 1	8 8 6 6			Controlled	Rest between sets (60-90 seconds)	Technique – good core set up. Maintain joint angle at knee.
Extra Option STANDING CALF RAISE	1 1	12 10			(2 : x : 1)	Rest between sets (60-90 seconds)	
LOWER ABS – HORSE STANCE	2	5 EACH LEG/ARM			Controlled	10SEC ON 10SEC OFF	Get correct start position. Maintain posture.

Key points: Notice that the reps have dropped to between 4 and 8 per set. The movements still have controlled down movements but have aggressive positive (up) movements. This is a good way to ensure that you are used to higher loads as you adjust to more power based movements

LS4B

UPPER BODY STRENGTH (CHEST/SHOULDERS) (Late Pre-Season)
Warm Up - 6-8 MINUTES GRINDING/BOXING/SHADOW BOXING/SPEED BALL ETC.

EXERCISE	SETS	REPS	WEIGHT	REPS	TEMPO	REST	GOAL / LOAD
FLAT BENCH PRESS	1 1 1 1 1	8 8 8 6 6			(2 : 0 : x)	Spot partner as rest between sets	Technique – ensure good position on bench and good bar control.
Superset with							
MEDICINE BALL or POWERBAG CHEST THROW (2 ARM)	1 1 1 1	8 8 6 6			Explosive	Rest between sets (60-90 seconds)	Explosive acceleration of the bar. Good core control
INCLINE DB PRESS	1 1 1 1	1 7 7 6 6			(2 : 0 : x)	Spot partner as rest between sets (60-90 seconds)	Technique – looking for good control of the dumbbells.
SPLIT STANCE MILITARY PRESS	1 1 1 1	S 8 8 6 6			(2 : x : 1)	Complete Split Stance Dumbbell Lateral Raise as super set	Technique – good set through core for stability. Lighter weight with good form.
Superset with							
SPLIT STANCE DUMBBELL LATERAL RAISE	1 1 1	10 8 8			Controlled	Rest between sets 60-90 seconds	Technique – good core set up. Arms to 90 degrees. Dumbbells parallel to floor.
SWISS-BALL RUSSIAN TWIST	3	6 L/R			Controlled	60-90 seconds	Good core set up. Hips parallel.

LS4C

UPPER BODY STRENGTH (BACK) (Late Pre-Season)

Warm Up - 4-6 MINUTES ROWING/SKIPPING
LIGHT LATPULLDOWNS (2 X 10)

EXERCISE	SETS	REPS	WEIGHT	REPS	TEMPO	REST	GOAL / LOAD
CHIN UP/PULL UP (WEIGHTED) (ALTERNATE REV CHIN AND WIDE GRIP FRONT CHIN)	1 1 1 1 1	Max. Max of 8 Max of 6 Max of 4 Max.			Controlled	Spot partner as rest between sets (90-120 seconds)	Technique – ensure good control. No more than 2 reps in the later sets. Change grip width and pattern. No leg swing.
BARBELL BENT-OVER-ROW	1 1 1 1	10 9 9 8 8			(1 : x : 1)	Rest between sets (60-90 seconds)	Technique – good set through core for stability.
1-ARM ON BENCH DB ROW	1 (L/R) 1 (L/R) 1 (L/R) 1 (L/R)	8 8 6 6			Controlled	Rest between sets (60-90 seconds)	Good stable setup. Don't use momentum in movement.
SWISSBALL BEARHUGS	2	6 (L & R)			(2 : 1 : 2)	60-90 seconds	Good core setup. Going left and right, up and down.

IPS5

POWER AND LEG STRENGTH (Late Pre-Season – Early In-Season)

Warm Up – 6-8 MINUTES ROWING/SKIPPING

GOOD MORNING (WITH BAR) (10 X 2), SWISSBALL SUPERMAN (8 X 2)

EXERCISE	SETS	REPS	WEIGHT	REPS	TEMPO	REST	GOAL
HANG CLEAN	1 1 1 1 1	8 6 6 4 4			Explosive	Rest between sets (120-180 seconds)	Technique – explosive bar speed with good control of core stability.
POWER CLEAN	1 1 1 1 1	6 4 4 3 3 3			Explosive	Rest between sets (120-180 seconds)	Technique – explosive bar speed with good control of core stability.
BACK SQUATS	1 1 1	8 6 6 4			(2 : 0 : x)	Complete Barbell Power Lunge as super set	Technique – ensure good depth and good control at bottom of the movement.
Superset with							
BARBELL POWER LUNGE	1 (L/R) 1 (L/R) 1 (L/R) 1 (L/R)	4 4 3 3			(2 : 0 : x)	Spot partner as rest between sets (60-90 seconds)	Technique – looking for good position on bench and good bar control.
SWISS BALL OBLIQUE SIDE RAISE	1 (L/R) 1 (L/R)	8 8			Controlled	Rest between sets (60 seconds)	Get correct start position. Bottom leg forward.

Core Conditioning

The concept of core strength and functional stability is an area where many myths and much misunderstanding are common. In the area of the abdominals and lower back, many people mistake what they can see with what is functionally important for use in maintaining good posture and safe, efficient movement. There are strong fads out there relating to body image and the desire for a "flat stomach" and the "6 pack".

Core strength/functional stability as it relates to the mid-section of the body, is the result of the interaction between the bones, muscles and attachments of both the abdominals and lower back. Abdominal and lower back musculature can act independently or as a unit when protecting and stabilizing your spine. Rugby requires considerable rotational and static strength. Scrummaging, tackling, and wrestling for the ball are all movements that require transfer of leg strength and power through the mid section to the upper body and shoulders.

While there are large numbers of videos and gimmicks out there that work on the abdominal region, it is worthwhile enlisting the help of a fitness trainer in consultation with this guide, to ensure that you perform exercises with good technique to get the best results.

Equipment recommended for purchasing to complete your core conditioning programme.

- **Swiss Ball / Gym Ball**
- **Medicine Balls**
- **Powerbag**

See the end of this chapter for core training programs.

Key Core Conditioning Exercises for Rugby

This section includes photographic insets of key core-conditioning exercises with instruction points to follow when performing each movement.

The following programmes cater for those of you who are new to core conditioning or untrained, through to those of you with advanced training experience and high levels of core strength. It is important to perform all exercises with correct technique and master the basic movements before progressing to more dynamic patterns of movement. Please note that even though you may be an experienced player with high levels of general fitness and strength you may still have poor core conditioning if you have never targeted this area in training - don't be afraid to start with the beginners programme.

Core Conditioning For Beginners

Targeted Area: Lower Abdominals
Exercise: 4 Point Abdominal Draw

Key Points:

- Draw the belly button towards the spine without changing the shape of the spine.
- i.e. make the waist as small as possible without rounding the back.

Targeted Area: Obliques
Exercise: Lying Side Raise

Key Points:

- Ensure the shoulders are in line and the movement is controlled.
- The elbow should be placed directly under the shoulder.
- The body is lifted until it is completely straight.
- Hold in the top position for up to 3 seconds.
- Lower back to the start position under control.

Targeted Area: Upper Abdominals
Exercise: Complex Crunch

Key Points:

- Left elbow goes to right knee. Stay up and right elbow goes to left knee.
- Return to the start position.
- Right elbow goes to left knee. Stay up and left elbow goes to right knee.

Targeted Area: Lower Back and Glut Strength
Exercise: Swiss Ball Hip Lower

Key Points:

- Head and shoulders starts on the ball.
- Lower leg is at right angles to the thigh.
- Ensure the hips are high. Lower to the bottom.
- Focus on activating the gluts to generate the movement back up to the start position.
- Movement should be controlled.

Targeted Area: Obliques
Exercise: Swiss Ball Oblique Side Raise

Key Points:

- Bottom leg is forward. Upper leg is back.
- Place both feet into the angle of the wall and floor.
- Place hip on the ball
- Place hands on your head or fold your arms across your chest.
- Movement of the shoulders should be in line with the hips.

Targeted Area: Functional Static Strength
Exercise: Swiss Ball Bear Hug

Key Points:

- Feet back and slightly wider than shoulder width. Arms hugging the ball.
- Maintain static hold as you role from side to side
- Hold in the outer position for up to 4 seconds.
- Good stability through your core.

Targeted Area: Functional Dynamic Strength
Exercise: Medicine Ball / Powerbag / Woodchopper

Key Points:

- Feet shoulder width apart. Weight shifts from one foot to the other.
- Ball travels at a 45 degree angle.
- Movement is generated with core, not arms.
- Important that chest stays up and core is stable.

Targeted Area: Lower Back and Glut Strength
Exercise: Prone Swiss Ball Leg Extension

Key Points:

- Body is positioned with the ball under the stomach.
- Elbows are on the ground.
- Legs are extended until the body is straight.
- Focus on using gluts to generate the movement.
- Feet and legs stay together.

Targeted Area: Lower Abdominals
Exercise: Horse Stance

Key Points:

• Hands below shoulders. Elbows in.
• Belly button drawn towards spine.
• Right angle between leg and torso.
• Head in a neutral position so neck and spine are in line.
• One hand and the opposite knee can be lifted to make the movement more advanced.

Targeted Area: Obliques
Exercise: Swiss Ball / Medicine Ball / Russian Twist

Key Points:

• Hips held high. Rotation is through the spine, not the arms.
• 90 degree angle at the knee joint.
• Head and shoulders are on ball.
• Arms are extended above the face holding the medicine ball.
• Hips stay up while generating movement through the spine.

Targeted Area: Upper Abdominals
Exercise: Swiss Ball/Medicine Ball/Powerbag/Sit-Up Throw

Key Points:

- Generate power for movement from the core, not the arms.

Targeted Area: Functional Static Strength
Exercise: Leaning Shoulder Drop

Key Points:

- Leaning person tries to stay rigid in their starting posture.
- Feet shoulder width apart.
- Partner places hand on either shoulder and leans the person to 30 – 40 degrees
- Partner should try to surprise them by releasing different hands.
- Leaning person must always attempt to come back to the starting position

Targeted Area: Functional Dynamic Strength
Exercise: Swiss Ball Wrestle (Partner)

Key Points:

- Try and stay on your feet.
- Use your core strength and grip to try and loosen the partners grip on the ball.
- A soft floor is preferable.

Targeted Area: Lower Back and Glut Strength
Exercise: Supine Table Top Balance

Key Points:

- Hips remain high. Feet are close together.
- Head and shoulders are comfortable on the ball.
- Take the balanced load of the body on one foot.
- Raise the other leg off the floor.
- Extend the leg straight out so that leg is straight.
- Hold in the extended position until you are sure you have balance.
- Come back slowly to the start position and complete the movement with the other foot.

Cross Training for Variety and Fitness

Cross training encompasses a wide range of the training modalities that exist today. There are many examples of cross training that can be carried out indoors or out.

A rugby player would be cross training if he/she were to do a spinning class, swimming, boxing, cycling, rowing or judo to name a few examples. An important point to note is that cross training to get fit to play rugby is nowhere near as effective as specific running, rugby training and wrestling. However, cross training is very useful to:

1. Add variety to reduce training boredom.
2. Maintain general fitness levels out of season with refreshing activities.
3. Cater for the effects of injury – maintain fitness while not loading an injured joint or body part.
4. Reduce the chances of overuse injuries while maintaining general fitness

Below are the most suitable cross training activities for rugby.

Treadmill Running Options (Flat and Incline):

How your muscles are activated on a flat treadmill is quite different from how we run on the ground. However, the similarity between these two different conditions increases as incline is added.

The hamstrings and gluteals become far more active with incline running on the treadmill, as they work to try and maintain your position on the running surface. Consequently, if you are looking for a better training effect, inclining the running surface is the way to go. Excessive incline and volume introduces high loads on Achilles and lower back structures so caution is required.

Ensure you know how to use a treadmill safely before attempting to run at speed.

TR1 Inclined treadmill running (undulating) – 32 minutes
Run a 5 minute warm-up and stretch.

TIME	SPEED	GRADIENT	TIME	SPEED	GRADIENT
4min hard	(11km/hr)	1%	3min easy	(10km/hr)	0%
3min hard	(12km/hr)	2%	2min easy	(10km/hr)	0%
2min hard	(13km/hr)	3%	1min easy	(10km/hr)	0%
1min hard	(14km/hr)	4%	1min easy	(10km/hr)	0%
2min hard	(13km/hr)	3%	1min easy	(10km/hr)	0%
3min hard	(12km/hr)	2%	2min easy	(10km/hr)	0%
4min hard	(11km/hr)	1%	3min easy	(10km/hr)	0%

TR2 Inclined treadmill running (Interval type) - 27 minutes
Run a 5 minute warm-up and stretch.

TIME	SPEED	GRADIENT	TIME
6min hard	(10km/hr)	0%	1min off
5min hard	(11km/hr)	1%	1min off
4min hard	(12km/hr)	2%	1min off
3min hard	(13km/hr)	3%	1min off
2min hard	(14km/hr)	4%	1min off
1min hard	(15km/hr)	5%	1min off

Stationary Cycle/Treadmill/Cross-country Skier:

Nearly all modern gym equipment software has built in session programmes. It is possible to get a hill profile and various other sessions from a treadmill, stationary cycle or cross-country skier. Program C1 at the end of this chapter features stationary cycle programmes.

C1 Cross-training (stationary cycle):
Will take 40 minutes on the cycle
Target: Lactate Stacking
Work/Rest: 3:1

5 minute warm-up TARGET WORK LEVEL					
Cycle	Rehab.	Med.	Hard	V.Hard	
9min hard (100+RPM)	L2-L4	L6	L7	L8	3min easy (70-80 RPM)
6min hard (100+RPM)	L3-L5	L7	L8	L9	2min easy (70-80 RPM)
3min hard (100+RPM)	L4-L6	L8	L9	L10	1min easy (70-80 RPM)
6min hard (100+RPM)	L3-L5	L7	L8	L9	2min easy (70-80 RPM)

C2 Cross-training (stationary cycle):
Will take 40 minutes on the cycle
Target: High intensity intervals
Work/Rest: 1:1

5 minute warm-up TARGET WORK LEVEL					
Cycle	**Rehab.**	**Med.**	**Hard**	**V.Hard**	
2min hard (100+RPM) **x4**	L3-L5	L8	L9	L10	2min easy (70-80 RPM)
1min hard (100+RPM) **x4**	L4-L6	L9	L10	L11	1min easy (70-80 RPM)
30sec hard (100+RPM) **x4**	L5-L7	L10	L11	L12	30sec easy (70-80 RPM)

Rowing Machine:

Rowing machines offer a good cross-training option because they combine and load legs, back, and arm strength. As a result they can be highly effective in improving general aerobic fitness and strength. Key points include focusing on the legs as the primary drivers of the movement, not pulling with the arms.

These programs are based on completion times for 500m of rowing at the stroke power and frequency that you are pulling at any given time. The working part of the session requires you to row for 6 minutes with a stroke rate between 28-32 per minute at a pace below 2.10sec for 500m followed by 3 minutes at a lower stroke rate above 2.10min 500m pace.

R1 Cross-training (concept 11 rower):
30 minutes on the rower
Target: High intensity intervals
Work/Rest: 2:1

5 minute warm-up			
Rower	**Stroke Rate**	**Intensity (500m pace)**	**Intensity (500m pace)**
6min hard	28-32	<2.00min 500m pace	3min easy >2.10min 500m pace
4min hard	28-32	<1.50min 500m pace	2min hard >2.10min 500m pace
2min hard	28-32	<1.40min 500m pace	1min easy >2.10min 500m pace
4min hard	28-32	<1.50min 500m pace	2min hard >2.10min 500m pace
6min hard	28-32	<2.00min 500m pace	3min easy >2.10min 500m pace

R2   *Cross-training (concept 11 rower):*

40 minutes on the rower
Target: High intensity intervals
Work / Rest: 1:1

5 minute warm-up			
Rower	Stroke Rate	Intensity (500m pace)	Intensity (500m pace)
2min hard	28-32 **x3**	<2.00min 500m pace	2min easy >2.10min 500m pace
1.5min hard	28-32 **x3**	<1.50min 500m pace	1.5min hard >2.10min 500m pace
1min hard	28-32 **x3**	<1.40min 500m pace	1min easy >2.10min 500m pace
30sec hard	28-32 **x3**	<1.30min 500m pace	30sec easy >2.10min 500m pace

Boxing/Kickboxing:

Boxing has become increasingly popular as a form of fitness for rugby. It is a great workout for the whole body but requires some expertise to master. Enlist the help of a personal trainer who either was a boxer or who has received training from a boxing coach so that you learn how to punch properly. Mixing it up with focus pads and bags makes for a good, intense and effective total body workout.

Swimming:

Swimming is a great total body work out to strengthen and maintain a degree of muscle tone, and is an excellent option if your training is restricted by a lower body injury. Some swimming tips:

- Goggles are an inexpensive purchase that will ease the strain on the eyes and increase comfort in the pool.
- The purchase, or hire of swimming aides (flippers, kickboards, paddles) will help to improve progress and increase or decrease the challenge of swimming depending on your level of expertise.
- Swimming lessons are a worthwhile investment if you need long-term recovery from injury.
- Attempt to incorporate and learn all the different strokes that are available. Freestyle, breaststroke and backstroke have less physical limitations attached to them than butterfly, which should be approached with caution.
- Break your lap swimming into intervals, see sample programme SW1. For example, you decide that you are going to swim 1500m in your session, don't just jump in the pool, warm-up and swim 60 lengths. The key advantage to swimming intervals is that it allows you to swim faster than you could if you swam continuously for the whole distance.
- Vary the number of strokes between each breath. This is called hypoxic training and could take the following form:

- 1st length - breathe every 2nd stroke
- 2nd length - breathe every 3rd stroke
- 3rd length - breathe every 4th stroke
- 4th length - breathe every 5th stroke
- 5th length - breathe every 5th stroke
- 6th length - breathe every 4th stroke
- 7th length - breathe every 3nd stroke
- 8th length - breathe every 2nd stroke

You might include this as part of an interval session.
- Base your session on a specific time period per length. i.e. you might decide to start a new length every 2 minutes regardless of how long it takes you to finish each length. For example if one length takes 1 minute you will have 1 minutes rest before the start of the next length.

SW1 Cross-training (swimming):
35-40 minutes in the pool

4 easy lengths to warm-up			
Swim	**Reps**		
10 lengths	**x 1**	(free-style)	60 second recovery
10 lengths	**x 1**	(hypoxic free-style)	60 second recovery
6 lengths	**x 4**	(free-style/breaststroke)	30 second recovery
8 lengths	**x 1**	(flippers/flutter board/breaststroke)	40 second recovery
2 length	**x 4**	(free-style)	20 second recovery

Aqua jogging/Aqua running:

Aqua jogging is an excellent cross-training option as you can apply running patterns in a non-weight bearing environment. Again in times of injury this can be a great option.

The key thing with aqua jogging, when using the aqua belt is to adopt a running position with the body straight but leaning slightly forward. Avoid the dog-paddle position. The legs must remain slightly behind but below the upper body. To increase the intensity take the aqua belt off, or conversely to make it easier wear two belts.

Joining a class creates variety and company, however ensure it is at an appropriate level for you. Those recovering from injuries will find that aqua jogging and stationary cycling are two of the first types of exercise that can be performed. The supportive nature of water makes it a great tool for recovery patterns as well.

Aqua running is a useful recovery activity following hard training sessions. It takes place in the shallow end of the pool so that water is approximately hip to waist deep. A series of running drills and a variety of movements including jogging, marching, lunging (front and sideways), running backwards, skipping, upper body rotations, and stretching can all be combined to achieve a good loosening of the body and reduction of aches and pains.

AQ1 Cross-training (aqua jogging):
35-40 minutes in the pool
Target: High intensity intervals
Work/Rest: Mixture

5 minute warm-up		
Aqua jog	**Reps**	
45sec hard15 seconds easy	**x 4**	1 minute recovery
30sec hard30 seconds easy	**x 6**	1 minute recovery
15sec hard30 seconds easy	**x 8**	1 minute recovery
30sec hard30 seconds easy	**x 6**	1 minute recovery
45sec hard15 seconds easy	**x 4**	1 minute recovery

Road Cycling and Mountain-Biking:

The same principles of variety that apply to running apply to cycling. However the non-weight bearing nature of both these types of cycling means that volumes can be much higher. Having toe clips is an advantage if you pedal actively (lifting on the leg coming up as the other leg pushes down) because it becomes a more positive workout.

Games:

Many popular forms of games (touch rugby, indoor netball, cricket and soccer) can be used as a form of cross-training to improve fitness and skill. They are great fun and will aid general fitness and competition just like the other cross-training options discussed.

Flexibility

Flexibility may aid in injury prevention and enhance sport and life performance. The following points are important to note when engaging in flexibility training.

- If the event you are stretching before is dynamic and powerful in nature (nearly all sports and any event that involves high running speeds) your stretching should be dynamic in nature (i.e. performed with movement). For example, a rugby player who kicks the ball should be gradually increasing leg swings in the patterns that are employed when kicking the ball.
- At the end of any event the stretching should be static in nature. This is stretching as people generally understand it, with long holds (20-30secs) in a fixed position at the outer limits of an individuals current range of motion. This is done on the premise that it prevents the muscles shortening and tightening as they cool down.
- Developmental stretching is done separate from the training session and generally includes static stretching and a variety of stretching called PNF (ask your local fitness expert for more information). The goal of this type of stretching is to actually increase the muscles range of motion.

Exercise: Dynamic Adductor Hurdle Stretch

Key Points:

- Good control of core
- Bring right leg up to the side and bring it forward as if stepping over a hurdle
- Place on the ground and repeat with the left leg
- Stretch can be done backwards but bring knee up and forward first, then backwards as if stepping over a hurdle

Exercise: Hamstring Ground

Key Points:

- Pull knee up and lace fingers under knee
- Bring foot up with toe pulled back until hamstring is under stretch.
- Pulse through this position using foot (up and down) or knee (push knee towards the sky)

Exercise: Hamstring Walk Up

Key Points:

- Feet flat on the ground
- Walk hands up towards feet as far as you can
- Finish position is when you can't maintain your hands and feet flat on the ground without bending arms or legs.
- Good ab control will help you with this stretch

Exercise: Hamstring with rotation

Key Points:

- Keep chest up and maintain natural curve in lower back
- Either push hands towards toes or generate a wide swinging movement

Exercise: Hip Flexor

Key Points:

- Front knee should remain over the front foot
- Upper body should be straight up and down
- Push back hip forward to get stretch on hip flexor
- Good control of core and hips is essential

Exercise: Squatting Adductor

Key Points:

- Good control of core is essential
- You can gently pulse at the bottom of the movement

Exercise: Lateral Stretch

Key Points:

- Keep shoulders in line with hips
- Do not pull head forward

Exercise: Lower back Stretch

Key Points:

- Important to keep shoulders on the ground
- Moving your top knee up will affect where on your lower back you feel the stretch

Exercise: Partner Leg Swing Start

Key Points:

- This dynamic range of motion exercise can be done with a partner or by yourself
- Good stability and control is required of the leg on the ground
- Can swing leg across the body or straight through (see photo).
- Need to maintain good upright position rather than leaning on your partner for support

Exercise: Partner Leg Swing Finish

Exercise: Partner Calf

Key Points:

- Keep back foot flat on ground
- Start with leg straight
- Bending the knee will shift the stretch in your calf (Soleus)

Exercise: Washing Machine

Key Points:

- A good exercise for stability and dynamic warm up with a partner
- Start in a squat position.
- Ensure you maintain natural curvature of your back
- Move arms back and forth using different speeds to increase the warmup effect.

Exercise: Quad Standing

Key Points:

- A good exercise for one legged balance
- Push the hip forward on the leg you are holding.
- Must maintain good, straight body position

Programme Options - Putting it all together

Training Smart

The key to fitness success is not just exercise, but how you combine workouts, job, recreation, nutrition and recovery. We want the tips and information included in this book to help you to integrate all these factors. We call this *"Training Smart"*.

Information in this chapter will explain:

- How to plan different exercises into a single training session.
- How to plan single training sessions into your training week.
- How to plan weekly training plans into long term training block.

Programming Tips

It is important to understand what impact one training session may have on your ability to train well the next day. We must aim to ensure that training sessions are planned in a way that achieves maximum training gains, prevents overuse injury, and achieves 100% recovery between sessions. This will ensure that you can train with intensity and quality for all workouts.

Generally speaking:

- Completing a heavy leg strength session will dramatically affect the quality of any running session you plan to do that day or the next.
- If you are training twice in the same day it makes sense to mix up workouts e.g. run in the morning and upper body weights in the afternoon.
- Having a day off is important. If you miss doing your session on that day and can't wait to get out there again, this is positive.
- Splitting up your body into body parts for weight training is a good way of maintaining variety and aiding recovery.
- Developing a system of coding your sessions allows for easier programming of your weeks and months. As you come up with new sessions you can add them to your list so that your training becomes a living document that grows with you, and your training history.
- Change your program on a regular basis, ideally every 4-6 weeks. This ensures your training does not reach plateau and continually changing the training stimulus will achieve greater training gains. New training stimulus is also important to keep your mind fresh and mentally challenged.

- Make your training <u>sustainable.</u> Don't let your lifestyle change be a flash in the pan. Not adhering to exercise is the biggest pitfall to most training programs. Players often fall down if their training schedule is too time consuming or difficult to maintain for a long period of time. Having a good rugby season requires consistent sustainable preparation that can be carried out around other life commitments.
- Reaching your training goals requires discipline and order. It is critical that you challenge the body and the mind with variations in planning and programming so that you remain motivated and your body receives the stimulus it needs to adapt and improve.

General Periodisation Guidelines

Rugby is a sport that requires total body conditioning combining a number of key fitness components. Before taking the field at the beginning of the season each fitness component needs to be targeted and maximised in the training time you have available.

In previous chapters we have outlined many training options, in this chapter we look at how you can put it all together to design a schedule that will prepare you for peak performance. Designing a training schedule that is made up of training months, weeks, and individual training sessions over a period of time is termed periodisation.

Periodisation for rugby can be broken into four main phases.

1	General Preparation	Off-Season
2	General Specific Preparation	Pre-Season
3	Specific Preparation	Pre-Season
4	Maintenance	In-Season

The following information is an overview of the key differences and planning considerations relating to each phase.

We discuss:
- What you are trying to achieve during each phase.
- The length of each training phase.
- Key areas to focus on as you move through training phases towards the start of the season.
- Sample training weeks.

Expert Comment

When you are working out your training plan it is best to work back from the first competition game in calculating how many weeks of training time you have available to you. However, you should also consider your warm-up games as they will have a considerable effect on your weekly training sessions as you approach the season.

Periodisation Planning Tables

BEGINNERS PERIODISATION No Previous Training Experience			
Components of Fitness	Off-Season (Times per week)	Pre-Season (Times per week)	In-Season (Times per week)
Aerobic Conditioning	2	1	
Anaerobic (Functional Conditioning)		1	1
Strength Training	1-2		
Power/Plyometrics			
Strength/Power/Core		2	1-2
Core Conditioning	1		
Speed/Agility		2	1
Flexibility/Pilates/Yoga	1	1	1
Cross Training	1 (extra)		
Specific Rugby Sessions		1-2	2-3
Total Sessions for the Week	6-7	7-8	6-8

INTERMEDIATE PERIODISATION
Some Training Experience

Components of Fitness	Off-Season (Times per week)	Pre-Season (Times per week)	In-Season (Times per week)
Aerobic Conditioning	2		
Anaerobic (Functional Conditioning)	1	2	1
Strength Training	1-2		
Power/Plyometrics		1	
Strength/Power/Core		2	1-2
Core Conditioning	1		
Speed/Agility	1	2	1
Flexibility/Pilates/Yoga	1	1	1
Cross Training	1 (extra)		
Specific Rugby Sessions		1-2	2-3
Total Sessions for the Week	**7-9**	**8-10**	**6-8**

ADVANCED PERIODISATION
High Level of Training Experience

Components of Fitness	Off-Season (Times per week)	Pre-Season (Times per week)	In-Season (Times per week)
Aerobic Conditioning	2		
Anaerobic (Functional Conditioning)	1	2	1
Strength Training	2-3		
Power/Plyometrics	1	1	
Strength/Power/Core		2	1-2
Core Conditioning	1		
Speed/Agility	1	3	1
Flexibility/Pilates/Yoga	1-2	1	1
Cross Training	1 (extra)		
Specific Rugby Sessions		1-2	2-3
Total Sessions for the Week	**9-11**	**9-10**	**6-8**

For example:

Preparation	Weeks remaining until first game		
	18 17 16 15 14 13	12 11 10 9 8 7	6 5 4 3 2 1
	Weeks to spend in training stage		
General (Off-Season)	6 5 4 3 2 1		
General Specific (Pre-Season)		6 5 4 3 2 1	
Specific (Pre-Season)			6 5 4 3 2 1
Maintenance (In-Season)			

Key Individual Considerations

Differences in this periodisation model can be considered first by your individual requirements and then by your positional needs. The reason for fitness testing is to find out where you are at with your fitness profile. Once you have a profile of your fitness you can then design your training programme to address your weaknesses.

Common Examples:

Strength Measures Poor / Aerobic Measures Good

Your fitness testing shows that you are not coming up to the strength measures. Both leg strength and power plus upper body strength are not meeting the desired standards. Obviously this is an area you need to give more attention to, and as such you may add an extra strength session instead of a running session during your off-season and pre-season programme.

Strength Measures Good / Aerobic Measures Poor

This is the opposite to the above situation. You may substitute a weights session for an extra running session. Often you need to consider your body composition and diet when this is the case. You may be carrying unwanted weight and shedding this will definitely help your cause.

Strength Measures Poor / Aerobic Measures Poor

You may adjust your focus from week to week to reduce interference. So in week 1 you may substitute a weights session for a running session and in week 2 you may reverse this. This may help you focus on each component separately and improve results in both areas at the same time.

Speed Measures Poor / Aerobic Measures Good

Speed is a difficult component to improve but you can get results by considering the following. Do an extra speed session instead of an aerobic conditioning session. Focus on speed and agility. Agility training will show quicker improvement than straight line speed and give you confidence on the field. Focus on anaerobic functional conditioning that includes repeated speed training. In this way you can improve your ability to maintain close to your maximal speed throughout the game so while others get tired you are still sharp.

Key Positional Considerations

Your coach and your own common sense will help you identify areas that you need to work on that relate to your position. Following is a table that identifies some key considerations for each different position on the field.

POSITIONAL FITNESS CONSIDERATIONS
Prop
A key part of your job as a prop is to scrummage. As such you need strength/power and mobility. You also need good strength above your head for overhead lifting. These factors need to be considered in your strength training programmes. You may require a certain weight to make you more competitive at scrum time but remember that good weight (muscle) not fat is the way to achieve this without compromising mobility.
Hooker
You also need to scrummage. Like the props you may require a certain weight to make you more competitive at scrum time but remember that good weight (muscle) not fat is the way to achieve this without compromising mobility. Remember a key area you are assessed on is lineout throwing so spend time on this facet of your training.
Lock
While you need to scrum you also need to jump in the lineouts. Plyometrics and jumping plus footwork drills will all contribute to your speed on the ground and your ability to get your own and the oppositions lineout ball. Strength and mobility are key for you as with the other tight forwards.
Loose Forward
Work rate in the form of functional conditioning and repeated-speed is critical to you on the field. You also need the speed/agility to get to breakdowns and the strength and power to be effective when you get there. Strength over the ball and the ability to rip and wrestle should be considered in your strength programming.

POSITIONAL FITNESS CONSIDERATIONS

Halfback

Work rate is a key in this position. Every ruck you are not at to clear the ball means someone else has to come in and take your position. To complement this you need the speed to get there quickly and the speed off the mark to take gaps around the ruck that are offered to you. Obviously your pass off the deck requires work.

1st Five

You need the fitness to help you make correct decisions when others are getting fatigued, speed off the mark to threaten the oppositions defensive line whenever you have the ball in hand, and strength and power to take the ball up if options are not available to you. Often you are the kicker so you need to dedicate time to this critical part of the game.

2nd Five / Centre

These positions require strength, speed, reasonable weight so you can pick holes to go through with the ball in hand, and the strength to hold onto it and place it well for quick ball. Defensively your strength, power and big hitting will be critical. Acceleration is an important area to work on as you often get the ball at three-quarter pace and must accelerate into the gap and holes in the opposition line.

Wing

Top end speed is a critical component, but you also need the ability to beat your man. Working on these patterns of agility and timing are important in your speed sessions. Functional conditioning and repeated-speed will help you maintain a high work rate in the game and ensure you have the fitness to come into the line when needed and cover defend as appropriate. Good strength, power will help you with ball security.

Fullback

Like the wingers top end speed is a critical component as is the ability to beat your man. Working on these patterns of agility and timing are important in your speed sessions. Functional conditioning and repeated speed will help you maintain a high work rate in the game and ensure you have the fitness to come into the line when needed and cover defend as appropriate. Good strength and power will help you with ball security especially when coming into the line.

General Preparation - Off-Season   (6-8 weeks)

Off-season gives you the time to build a strong foundation and develop base conditioning. This base work includes general aerobic fitness, strength, core stability, and speed technique. During this phase of your season, you should be targeting five to six training sessions per week.

A key word with off-season fitness work is variety. If you have a hard game of touch, squash, or tennis then count that as part of your program but be realistic about how hard it was. For example, if you had programmed to complete 3 running based conditioning sessions each week and you played a hard game of touch rugby you may count this as one of these sessions.

Developing your Off-Season Aerobic Base

Swimming, aqua-jogging, and cycling are all good aerobic conditioning options. However, rugby is a running based sport and it is recommend that for training specificity running is to make up the majority of your off season aerobic sessions.

As you work through your off season running programme ensure you overload by way of running speed, length of sessions and using interval training. Training options A1, A2, and A3 will get your aerobic training started, use these workouts for the first 2-3 weeks. As you fitness increases progress to workouts A4, A5, and A6 to overload and further enhance your base fitness.

Developing your Off-Season Strength Base

At this stage of your season your goal is to develop strength and strength endurance using resistance training. The options included in the weight training chapter offer programmes targeting different training objectives.

If you are looking for strength gains there are 2 and 3 day split routine combinations to follow. Aim for 3-4 strength sessions per week. An example weekly strength session plan may include S1A, S1B, and S1C over three different days. Another option could include completing S2A and S2B sessions twice during each week.

Example two week resistance training block:

Week 1

Mon	Tues	Weds	Thurs	Fri	Sat	Sun
Aerobic	Strength	Aerobic	Strength	Rest	Strength	Rest
A1	S1B	A3	S1C		S1A	

Week 2

Mon		Tues		Weds /Speed		Strength/ X-Training		Fri		Sat		Sun	
Strength		**Aerobic**		**Aerobic**		**Strength/**		**Strength**		**Aerobic**		**Rest**	
am	pm	am	pm	am	pm	am	pm	am	pm	am	pm	am	pm
S2A		A3	S2B	SA1	R1	S2B	SW1	S2A		A3			

Note: SA1 = Position Specific Speed/Power

These two examples show you that you do not have to look solely at 7 day or weekly training blocks. You may plan a two week training block to vary your training. The above example sees week 1 completing 2 aerobic and 3 strength sessions, and week 2 completing 4 strength sessions, 2 aerobic sessions, 1 cross training and 1 speed/agility session.

Please note:
Flexibility and core conditioning are not specifically set out in the above example training weeks. It is expected and recommended the flexibility work is a consistent component of all sessions. Core conditioning can be carried out as part of your strength sessions or completed as stand alone workouts to be completed at least 3-4 times each week.

Expert Comment

When you are working out your training plan it is best to work back from the first competition game in calculating how many weeks of training time you have available to you. However, you should also consider your warm-up games as they will have a considerable effect on your weekly training sessions as you approach the season. The number of weeks you spend in each training phase will depend on how much time you have before the start of the season.

Specific Preparation - Pre-Season (2 blocks of 6 weeks)

Pre-season is time to start fine tuning your base work and progress your training to reflect the more specific demands of rugby. Focus should shift to interval style recovery training, speed development, power development and include skill work.

Generally speaking we aim to reduce the total volume of training and increase the training intensity. Nearly all of your aerobic conditioning work should now be made up of running options. Speed and agility becomes very important as does specific power development. The key words with pre-season training are intensity and quality.

Refining and Maintaining your Aerobic Base

Running is the main option for maintaining your aerobic base. A4, A5, and A6 should dominate through this period. You may only get one session per week targeting this component.

Building Anaerobic Power and Capacity

Interval training will now dominate as we must become conditioned to cope with the repeated high intensity efforts that make up passages of play. Use the repeated speed (RS) options to improve your ability to sprint repeatedly and recover quickly.

Start out with the longer intervals such as RS1 and RS2 and progress into the shorter options such as RS5, RS6, and RS7 to improve your ability to work at a high intensity and recover quickly.

Refining your Strength Base

At this stage of your season your goal is to develop maximal strength and power. During these two 6 week blocks you can begin to use the PS1A and PS1B power/strength options to refine your training patterns.

Example early pre-season weekly schedule:

	Mon	Tues	Weds	Thurs	Fri	Sat	Sun
	Speed/ Strength	Aerobic	Interval	Strength	Speed/ Strength	Aerobic/ Interval	Rest
am	SA1	A3	RS3	ES3B	SA2	A5	
pm	ES3A				ES3C		

Note: SA2 = Position Specific Speed/Quickness

Example late pre-season two weekly schedules:

	Mon	Tues	Weds	Thurs	Fri	Sat	Sun
	Power/Speed		Intervals	Power	Speed	Functional	Rest
am	Speed - Option1 SA2 Quickness		RS5	PSB1	Speed - Option1 SA1 Power	FE1	
pm	PS1A	Team or A6		Team or RS4			

	Mon	Tues	Weds	Thurs	Fri	Sat	Sun
	Power/Speed		Intervals/Power	Speed	Intervals	Aerobic	Rest
am	Speed - Option2 SA2 Quickness			Speed - Option1 SA1 Power		A6	
pm		Team	PS1B	Team			

Maintenance – In-Season

The key word with in-season fitness work is maintenance. You should be aiming for a minimum of two and up to four sessions per week on top of your club practice sessions, plus a recovery session the day after the game.
Target getting all your training done between Sunday and Thursday with Friday off for recovery, so that when you play on Saturday you are feeling fresh.

Maintaining your Aerobic Base

Running is the preferred option for maintaining your aerobic base. Use A3 and A6 options to achieve this. The functional endurance FE1 session is a great option for maintaining all parts of your conditioning profile. Many teams now use conditioning games. This includes games like modified touch rugby to make it more rugby specfic.

Maintaining Anaerobic Power and Capacity

Use the shorter options such as RS6, RS7 and RS8 occasionally to sharpen up your fitness as the season progresses.

Maintaining your Strength Base

You will probably only have time for a maximum of two gym sessions per week, so include components of strength and power in your sessions. Do your power work first and then continue on with strength e.g. PS1A and PS1B. If you only have a chance to do one session then you will need to cover the whole body during the one workout. Be aware that you will struggle to maintain power/ strength and muscle mass with only one session per week.

Sample in season weekly schedule

The number of sessions completed in season will depend on available training time.

	Mon	**Tues**	**Weds**	**Thurs**	**Fri**	**Sat**	**Sun**
	Power/Funct.		Intervals		Speed		
am	PS1A		RS7		Option2 SA2 Quickness	Game	Recovery
pm	FE1	Team	PS1B	Team			

The big mistake that many players make is to believe that two team practices and one game per week will maintain their pre-season fitness levels. Your match fitness will increase to a point with games, but all other components of fitness (strength, power, speed) will fall off if untrained, resulting in your match fitness being negatively affected. If training time is limited target strength/ power sessions as the priority and complete speed based sessions before or after team training.

Another important factor is to avoid overtraining. Overtraining is where your body is given insufficient time to recover and adapt between sessions leading to poor training results and decreased game performance due to fatigue. If you do too much work in-season then the games themselves will be adversely affected. You should be able to cope with a total of five to six sessions per week and one light and easy recovery session.

Note: Over reaching is like a short term overtraining effect. If you continuously over reach you will experience overtraining. Over reaching may affect you negatively for a number of days. Overtraining can affect you for weeks.

New Training Innovations

The new and professional face of rugby has seen the evolution of a growing number of modern training innovations. Coaches and players have a myriad of new training aids available to them having come about through advancements in technology or sports science.

At the time of completing this book (2005) three training inventions of particular merit have become accessible to forward thinking players and coaches. These selected performance aids are now widely accepted in rugby as conditioning and skill development tools. The past 12 months has seen the sport of rugby quickly incorporate these systems into all player levels.

In the interests of providing readers with the most up to date, recent and widely used training developments we have included brief information in this chapter.

Powerbags™

Powerbags are weighted, hardwearing, soft, flexible resistance training bags with carry handles. The tubular bags are made up of the same material as tackle bags so can be used indoors or outside, in any weather conditions. It has a soft foam inner so that it is safe and easy to carry and catch for running and power throwing drills. Inside the foam a sand bag is used to weight the bag. Weights vary from 3kg-50kg.

Powerbags seem to combine all the benefits of strength and power exercises commonly performed with barbells, dumbells and power and functional training commonly performed with medicine balls. This is due to the multi purpose aspects of the device that enables it to be lifted like weights, or thrown like a medicine ball. Powerbags also allow players to develop rugby specific rotational power which is unique to the training tool.

- Lunge with rotation
- Power Press Up

Generally speaking the portability of Powerbags mean players and coaches can take any exercise usually performed inside in the gym, outside to the rugby training field. Strength and power training is no longer limited to separate indoor sessions and power can be developed as part of an outdoor team training session with Powerbags.

They are also ideal for loaded fitness, speed, core stability, strength games and plyometric drills. Powerbags open up a whole new era of resistance training options and are quickly growing in popularity.

See www.power-bag.com to find out more about this training system.

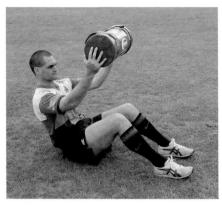

• Sit Up Throw

• Upright Row

• Double Bag Squat

• Front Squat

• Front Push Press

Skill-Tec™

The Skill-Tec™ training system is a skill development rugby ball developed in South Africa. It allows players to practise passing, kicking and catching skills in real time without a team mate or training partner.

The patented system uses interchangeable flexible leads connected to the ball via a swivel that returns the ball back to you as if being passed or kicked by a team-mate.

The ball will spiral naturally off the foot or hand as a real match ball would, so true game situation skills can be practiced by individuals.

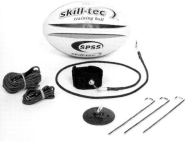

NAVMAN© GPS Sport Tool

GPS technology has developed markedly over a very short time with the technology now being at a level where it can contribute to enhancing sports performance. There are now GPS training devices available that allow you to very accurately monitor and assess any running or cycling based training.

GPS technology can literally record what you are doing at the time of training and assess exactly what you have done post training. This technology is capable of revolutionising training monitoring, motivation, and fitness testing.

The NAVMAN Running Sport Tool is designed to track and record exact distance run, real time current speed, average speed, current pace, average pace, lap times and calories burned. You can literally track how far you have run and how fast you have run.

The GPS technology can also be programmed to set maximum and minimum speeds. The alarm feature indicates if you are running too fast or too slowly to achieve the programmed set speed.